D0313089

Depression is a Liar

It is *possible to recover and be happy again –*

even if you don't believe it right now

By Danny Baker

Text copyright © 2013 Danny Baker

All Right Reserved

For being the inspiration behind the Depression Is Not

Destiny Campaign, I'd like to dedicate this book to Samantha

Jade.

Sammi, you have touched me in a way you can never imagine,

and I hope in my own way I can do the same for others.

PROLOGUE

~~~

I picked up the sharpest piece of glass I could find on the side of the road and put it to my throat.

'No!' someone screamed, running towards me.

'Stay back!' I yelled, holding out the glass.

The man froze, raising his hands in the surrender sign.

'Pl-please . . .' he stuttered. 'Please don't do this. Whatever happened . . . it can be fixed.'

'What the fuck do you know?' I yelled. 'You don't know what it's like to be me! You're not crazy! You don't want to kill yourself one week and chase hallucinations the next! What the fuck do you know? What the *fuck* do you know?'

'OK, OK,' he motioned, patting the air. 'I'm sorry. Just please don't do this. *Please.*'

The crowd all tried to talk me into dropping the glass, but once again I brought it to my neck. I pierced the skin, felt hot blood dripping onto my hand.

Death. I craved it, craved it.

It was like a maddening hunger that I wanted to feed so badly. Everything was just so fucked up. Everything had been fucked up for so long and I was sure that this was the only way out. There was nothing I wanted to do but satisfy that craving. Nothing I wanted to do but die. Running that piece of glass over my throat made me feel better, thinking that the craving's about to be fed, thinking that the pain's about to end. So close to the apathy of death. Nothingness! The end! An escape at last!

Plunge it through your throat! Through your fucking throat! Now! Now!

My hand trembled wildly. My whole body shook.

Do it! Kill yourself! End it now!

My hand kept trembling and trembling before finally, the glass slipped through my fingers and fell to the ground. I couldn't do it. I exploded into tears, cried loudly as all my emotions ruptured inside me—in large part because I knew I'd have to keep living and fighting in this crazy fucked up world—but regardless, I knew I couldn't do it. I'm just not a quitter. When it really comes down to it I'm just not a quitter.

A couple of people helped me to my feet, moved me away from the wreckage. I sat hugging my shins on the sidewalk, crying with my head buried in my knees as the crowd watched on silently.

'You're not a quitter,' I kept sobbing to myself. 'You're not a quitter.'

The police arrived. They asked me what happened.

'You're not a quitter,' I kept repeating.

'So fix this.'

Taking a deep breath, I did my best to gather myself before looking up at the officers. And then I told them what happened.

'I'll plead guilty to whatever offence you see fit to charge me with,' I said when I had finished. 'But first, I need to be admitted to a psych ward.'

~~~

The above excerpt is actually the prologue of my as yet unpublished novel *I Will Not Kill Myself, Olivia*.

'What's your book about?' everyone would ask me while I was writing it.

An informative answer might've been that it is a tale of lost innocence, of a boy-going-on-man being sucked so deep into the vortex of depression that he self-destructs almost to the point of death; that it is a book about breakages—both psychological and romantic— yet also one about second chances; and that above all else, it is the story of Jimmy, of Olivia, and of the love that binds them.

But at the time, I didn't want to be informative.

'It's just a messy love story,' I'd mutter before quickly changing the subject.

My novel wasn't something I liked talking about because while I was working on it, I was afraid of being asked the inevitable question:

'What gave you the idea to write about mental illness?'

I don't like lying, and that wasn't a question I was comfortable answering honestly. I wasn't ready to tell anyone that I was just writing what I know—that while my protagonist Jimmy is his own character in his own world, that the apple, so to speak, did not fall far from the tree. I wasn't ready to tell anyone that the only reason I could write authentically about depression—and the alcoholism, drug abuse, medicine-induced psychosis, near-suicide attempts and hospitalisations it can lead to—was because I'd experienced it all myself. I was still in the thick of it. Still trying to get better. I didn't want anyone but the people closest to me knowing what I was going through.

I was gradually able to recover, however, and by the time I'd finished my novel at the end of 2012, I was happy, and ready to be open about my plight to try and help others who were suffering like I had. At the same time I was starting to think about finding a publisher, and that's when I came up with the Depression Is Not Destiny Campaign, to inspire victims of the illness to never give up on happiness. It centres around a video blog following my quest to get *I Will Not Kill Myself, Olivia* published, which will hopefully culminate in the moment when I am offered a contract. Through my blog and this memoir I want everyone to know what I went through, to understand how I recovered, and to be there with me when I hopefully achieve my dream of becoming a published author; if and when it happens, I want everyone to see how overwhelmingly happy I'll be, I want everyone to literally see the tears of joy streaming down my cheeks, because it will show them that depression is beatable, and that even the most severely afflicted can overcome it and go on to live happy, healthy, fulfilling lives. I think seeing me come full-circle—from on the brink of suicide to achieving my dream—will give others hope that they can do the same.

So with that in mind, this is my story—told as candidly as I can possible write it. I hope that after reading it, you'll understand why I'll be so emotional if and when my novel gets published, and I hope you'll be there with me in that wonderful moment of bliss.

PART I

OR

WARNING SIGNS

OR

I DID *NOT* RAPE HER

March, 2007

At the annual Sydney University Scholarship Dinner I got talking to Mr Williams, one of my old high school teachers who'd been invited by the faculty.

'So how've you been, Danny?' he asked.

'Top of the world, Mr W! I'm really happy to be studying Commerce/Law, and I've also started writing my first novel called *Chrysalis* about an orphan's plight in the Great Depression of the 1930s. This year's going to be great! I'm going to get a High Distinction average[1] across all of my subjects and have my novel published by the end of the year! And when I finish my degree, I'm going to become a rich investment banker or management consultant and travel all over the world and live up the high life! It's going to be incredible! I can't wait to jump right into it!'

I kept talking, giddy with excitement as Mr Williams listened indulgently. At some point the mains were served, after which the scholarship holders were called up on stage and presented with awards.

'Congratulations, Danny,' Mr Williams said back at our table. 'You did really well to get such a coveted scholarship. I know you worked hard for it, and you deserve it as much as anyone.'

'Thanks,' I said.

'You've been blessed with so much,' he continued. 'You've been brought up in a wonderful neighbourhood; you're surrounded by a loving, supportive family; and you've got the opportunity and the ability to do anything you want to in life.'

He paused for a moment.

'I hope you use your blessings for good,' he said. 'I hope you always do charity work, and I hope you always try to help people.'

He paused again.

[1] In the US, this is approximately equivalent to a Grade Point Average equal to or greater than 3.9 out of 4.0.

'Remember, Danny: to whom much is given, much is expected.'

May, 2007

For all my lofty ambitions, however, it was to my great dismay that my first semester of uni was a struggle from the start. Whenever I studied as much as I needed to in order to get a High Distinction average, I hardly got any writing done. Whenever I stuck to writing—which was most of the time—I fell behind at uni; I'd missed weeks of class and hadn't done even half of the readings for each subject. Playing on the uni basketball team, tutoring high school students and getting smashed on the town two or three nights a week didn't help either, but I was never going to use that as an excuse.

I was so frustrated with myself for being so far behind. I felt so guilty for not working harder. I took pride in being an accomplished person who achieved my goals, so going off the rails like that was completely unacceptable. I hated myself for it.

But the exams were still a few weeks away, so I had time to recover. *If I pull some all-nighters I should be able to catch up and get my High Distinction average,* I thought. *I'll be OK. This is what caffeine is meant for.*

July, 2007

Fucking hell! I swore when I got my exam marks back. *Fuck me dead! An average of 74%! That's fucking terrible! That's 11% off my goal! What a disgrace. What an embarrassment. I fucked up this semester. I failed.*

I was so angry with myself. Once again I felt so guilty for not working harder. And rubbing salt into the wound was the fact that all the other scholarship holders kicked my ass. It made me feel so inadequate. It made me feel so ashamed of myself.

I told Mum how disappointed I was. She couldn't believe it.

'But Danny you were writing so much that you hardly studied!' she exclaimed. 'All things considered you still did really well! How can you possibly be so hard on yourself?'

But that wasn't how my mind worked. The way I saw it, if you set a goal and didn't reach it, then it meant you failed. It was like that when I got 99.6 instead of a perfect 100 for my UAI[2] at the end of school, and it was like that then, too.

I need to work harder next semester, I told myself. *I need to work harder so that I can get my writing done and still have time to study for my exams and get the marks that I want to get. If I work harder, then I won't feel this pain ever again. If I work harder, then I'll end up getting a High Distinction average and writing a great novel of publishable quality and then everything will be fine. It really is that simple. I just need to work harder.*

---

[2] University Admissions Index—equal to the percentile in which one is ranked in the state of New South Wales, as calculated by one's performance in the Higher School Certificate, completed in Year 12.

August, 2007

I met Chanel at the beginning of the next semester. It started how it often does at that age—being introduced, getting to know each other a bit, flirting at uni and then hooking up one Saturday night at a club before jumping straight into a relationship. When it happened I was imbued with a pulsing rush; this was a new world to me—I'd never had a proper girlfriend before—and Chanel was glamorous and beautiful and intelligent and I wanted to be with her.

Our first official date was in the city on a cloudless sunny day. We found ourselves holding hands across the table at lunch, strolling through Hyde Park with our arms around each other, sharing a big bowl of mixed gelato and feeding each other spoonfuls, and then making out beneath the trees at the Royal Botanic Gardens. We just felt so comfortable together, like we'd been a couple for years instead of only a week. In the afternoon we sat hand in hand on the grass and leapt into each other's souls, and I found myself telling her things I'd hardly spoken of before. I told her about how I'd always wanted to be a professional basketball player, and about how gut-wrenchingly devastated I was when my knee blew out in Year 10 and ruined my chances. I told her how that up until then I never bothered studying and always came in the bottom 10% of the year, and that once I'd injured my knee and had no chance of going pro anymore, nearly everyone at my snooty private school (including most of my friends) said that I was washed up and would amount to nothing; I told her that they all looked down on me so much and made me feel so inadequate that I vowed to start studying really hard and kick all their asses in Year 12. I told her that even though high school was ancient history, that the whole experience had ignited this lasting obsession in me to want to beat everyone in everything I did, to always want to be the best, to always want to be the guy that everyone looked up to instead of being the chump that everyone ridiculed and laughed at. Chanel listened, she understood, she shared the tribulations she'd been through. It all just happened so naturally, with an intimacy and tenderness deeper than any I'd ever known.

When night had blanketed the sky, I walked her to her platform at Central Station. We looked into each other's eyes, and for the first time I realised how spectacularly blue hers were, how easy it was for me to lose myself in them. We kissed until her train came, and as I watched her board the carriage and the vehicle grow smaller and smaller in the distance, I remember feeling the tug of love at my heart, a dazed sort of bliss I'd never experienced before. I remember having a really good feeling about her. A really, really good feeling indeed.

September, 2007

It had all started off so sublimely. I was convinced I'd found everything I'd ever wanted in a woman, and that our love would burn brightly for the years to come. But then a sickening notion infected my mind, and began to fill me with an anxious dread.

I think Chanel has something going on with one of my best mates.

She'd keep denying it, but I'd see the way Brad and her would look at each other. I knew they talked on the phone all the time. *And if nothing is going on*, I'd think, *then why does she always invite him to hang out with us? Why does she at other times blow me off to spend time with him?*

We'd fight about it all the time.

'I'm telling you, we're just *friends*,' she'd always say. 'Why do you keep putting me through all this arguing? You're a dickhead for accusing me of liking him. If you really loved me, you'd believe me.'

She'd always manage to guilt me into feeling like an asshole and letting the matter drop, and I'd find myself hanging up the phone thinking I was the bad guy.

She's right, I'd tell myself. *I'm being a jerk for not trusting her. I'm implying that she's a shit person by accusing her of two-timing. How must that make her feel? . . . But still! This just doesn't make sense! The way she's acting, something* must *be going on!*

It was such a maddening situation. Day after day it would persecute my mind. The good times—the Botanic Gardens days—became fewer and farther between, and our relationship gradually disintegrated into one big fight. Instead of being a blessing, I came to view love as a torturous curse.

~~~

I was binge drinking a lot those days, 20 standard drinks a night two or three times a week. I'd always embodied the "work hard, play hard" mantra, and getting wasted was my favourite way to wind down after an intense week of studying and writing. To my parents it was a constant cause of concern, but I was convinced I had everything under control.

'I'm just being an 18 year old,' I'd say whenever they'd reproach me about my drinking. 'Plus I work so hard during the day, so that gives me the right to cut loose at night.'

Not to mention, I'd think, *that all the fighting with Chanel is driving me nuts.* It seemed like that's all we ever did. Non-stop. All the time. Twenty-four/seven.

For fuck's sake, I remember thinking, *I'm studying Commerce/Law, I'm writing a novel, and my girlfriend who I adore is probably fucking my friend. So don't I deserve a bottle of bourbon to relax?*

October, 2007

Chanel and I eventually broke up. She finally admitted she had feelings for Brad, so that was it. I was heartbroken. When I was alone after it happened I burst into tears, cried long and hard into the palms of my hands. I was so overwrought. So shattered. I'd lost the woman I loved and I was absolutely gutted.

'Fuck Chanel,' my mates from school would say. 'She was making you miserable anyway. Just forget about her and that whole uni crowd. Come out with us, meet another chick, have a rebound fling. Start having fun again, man. We've never seen you this unhappy before.'

So I started spending more time with my school friends again, hanging out at their houses and going to parties with them. It was hard-going at first—I was missing Chanel like crazy and I just wanted to be with her. But after a few weeks, I began to turn the corner. I started forgetting about Chanel and got back to enjoying a life of studying, writing, playing basketball and chilling with the boys. I started realising that maybe I didn't need her, that my life was actually better without all the fighting and the drama. I even met another girl at a party and was contemplating asking her out, but then Chanel caught wind of it and hit the roof.

'I can't believe you're going to start dating someone else already!' she yelled into the phone. 'It's only been *three* weeks!'

'Are you kidding me? Chanel, *you're* the one who broke up with me because you said you liked Brad.'

'I didn't think you'd start seeing someone so soon!'

'What did you expect me to do? Spend the rest of my life crying over you?'

'No, but—'

'Why are we even having this conversation? Shouldn't you be off fucking Brad?'

'Don't say that!'

'Why not?'

'Look—I made a mistake, OK?'

'What are you talking about?'

She went on to say that she'd been really confused—that at the time we broke up she wasn't sure what she wanted, but that since then she'd had a chance to figure everything out. She said that she no longer had feelings for Brad—that that was all well and truly over with and was just one big mistake. And then she said she still had feelings for me.

Like a dog that'd been kicked in the morning but then petted at night, I was exhilarated, and had completely forgotten about the way Chanel had previously stomped on my heart. I was a sucker in love, and hearing her say that she still liked me was heavenly music to my ears.

'So do you want to go out again?' I asked excitedly.

'I can't,' she said.

My heart dropped.

'Why not?'

She said she wasn't ready to be in a relationship yet—that she needed some time to focus on herself.

'But I will be ready soon, though, and I want you to wait for me until then.'

I felt uneasy straight away.

'You . . . you want me to . . . *wait* . . . for you?' I asked hesitantly.

'Yes.'

'Well . . . I mean . . . how long for?'

'Not very long. Just until the end of the semester.'

'Why can't we just go out now?'

'I told you—I'm not ready yet.'

'Why not?'

'I don't know. I'm just not.'

I was suspicious. What she was saying just didn't make sense. And I still didn't fully trust her after the Brad fiasco.

She sensed my reservations.

'Danny . . . why are you being so misunderstanding?'

'I'm trying to understand, but—'

'I thought you loved me. Can't you just do this one little thing for the woman you love?'

More guilt trips. More manipulation. With hindsight, I shouldn't have capitulated. I shouldn't have let myself get sucked back into a situation that I didn't feel comfortable in. But I was blinded by love and wanted nothing more than to be with her.

'OK, Chanel,' I said. 'I'll wait for you.'

~~~

As per our "agreement", we weren't together, but we also weren't allowed to be with anyone else, and there was the clear understanding that we'd be a couple again as soon as Chanel was "ready for a relationship".

I hated it.

Breaking up with her was devastating, but at least I had closure and could begin to heal by moving on. Under this new set of circumstances however, I got the worst of both worlds. I was stuck in no man's land. I was miserable.

'I can't stand this, Chanel,' I'd tell her. 'There's too much uncertainty . . . too much that can go wrong. I mean, what if you decide you don't want to commit to me? What if you decide you'd rather be with Brad instead?'

'Danny how many times do I have to tell you? There's nothing going on between me and Brad! We're just friends! I want to be with *you*, OK. I just need you to wait for me until I'm ready.'

'I hate this waiting . . . you know I hate it.'

'Yeah, I know. But if you love me, you'll do it.'

And so I did. And so throughout October, I grew more and more anxious, I grew more and more melancholy, and this sorrow poisoned the rest of my life. It made it so difficult to study. It made it so difficult to write. I started falling behind all over again, and I was fucking livid with myself for it.

Do you want all the other scholarship holders to kick your ass again? I'd ask myself. *Do you want to feel inadequate again? Do you want to feel like a failure again? No? Then fucking pull yourself together and knuckle down and focus!*

But no matter how hard I tried I just couldn't manage to do it. Chanel was tearing me apart—so much so that at times I thought I should just forget about her and call it quits for good.

If I was single, I rationalised, *then I'd be able to focus and achieve my goals, and then I wouldn't feel so disappointed and frustrated and angry with myself all the time.*

But I couldn't leave her. For whatever reason, I thought she was "the one". At times I really, genuinely, thought she was the one. I clung to the belief that we were just going through a rough patch—that we'd soon get through it and it would all be worth it.

She knows how much I care about her, I convinced myself. *She'd never do anything to hurt me. We're going to get married and spend the rest of our lives together.*

So it's over. And given that it is, you have no right to get pissed off with me for talking to other chicks.'

'I'm not pissed off. I just got so jealous seeing you talk to another girl.'

'Why did you get jealous?'

'Because I still have feelings for you.'

'Then why aren't we dating then?'

'I told you! I don't want to date anyone right now.'

'Even though you have feelings for me?'

'Yes.'

I sighed.

'Does this have anything to do with Brad?'

'Shut the fuck up about Brad!' she screamed. 'How many times do I have to tell you it's got nothing to do with him?'

For a while, no-one spoke. Immeasurable frustration hung in the air as we both brooded in silence.

'So we like each other, but we're not going to date,' I eventually summed up. 'So where does that leave us?'

'I don't know,' she shrugged.

December, 2007

So there I found myself again, trapped between a rock and a hard place—that insufferable no man's land I'd so hated before.

'I'm so confused,' Chanel would always say. 'I know I have feelings for you, but I just don't want to be in a relationship right now. This is crazy, Danny . . . I have no idea what to do. Nothing makes sense to me anymore.'

I had it in my mind that the reason she didn't want to be with me was because she was scared—of commitment, of intimacy, of who knows what. So I stuck it out hoping that she'd come around, miserable day after miserable day. The pain of not being with her, of knowing she was single and could be hooking up with any given guy at any given time was so tormenting that over the course of the month, I gradually lost my ability to function. I could hardly write. I could barely eat. I'd lie up night after night unable to fall asleep.

This isn't worth it, my head would tell me. *Just make a clean break for it and forget Chanel ever existed.* But my heart was telling me that she was beautiful, that she was special, that she was my one true love, and that it was worth doing whatever it took to make it work with her.

By the end of the month, however, I couldn't take it anymore. I'd devolved into an exhausted shell of myself, a nauseous wreck of a person who was rapidly withering away. Something had to give. Something had to change.

'I can't do this anymore,' I finally told her. 'It's just too much uncertainty, too much worrying, too much pain. I need to know where I stand with you—once and for all this time.'

I sighed.

'So I'm going to give you until New Year's Eve to work out what you want. If you decide you want to be with me, then that's great. But if you don't, then I'm done for good. I'm moving on. For real this time.'

New Year's Eve, 2007

From the moment I woke up I was stricken with nerves, so I went to a friend's place to drown them in alcohol. I spent the day getting pissed playing beer pong with my school mates, doing my best to enjoy myself instead of tensely counting down the hours until night when I was due to meet Chanel at a party. By five o'clock I'd had half a dozen beers and a bottle of bourbon, and was able to escape by passing out on the couch. But when I woke up it was seven and time to go, and once again I was consumed with apprehension.

The boys and I arrived and joined the other guests on the balcony. We sat in a circle and talked for a while, drinking beers and passing joints as my anxiety heightened.

This is it, I kept telling myself. *She's going to be here any minute. I'm only moments away from knowing whether she'll be my girlfriend or an ex I'll never speak to again. Soon I'm going to be either deliriously happy or miserably devastated.*

A touch after eight she arrived with some friends, looking beautiful as ever wearing a white strapless dress and red high heels. I walked up to her and gave her a peck on the cheek, and said hello to the rest of her friends. A couple of my mates then went to greet her, and one of them ended up talking to her in a corner of the room for 20 minutes. He came to speak to me straight afterwards.

'You're in, mate,' he said. 'It's gonna be fine.'

I mixed up another big bottle of bourbon and cola and finally got talking to her myself. She was shooting me flirtatious looks, teasing me playfully, rubbing my arm whenever she spoke. The vibe was good. The signs were all there. At some point we got drawn into a drunken group hug, and as we pulled away, our eyes locked. Our heads moved closer together. And then for the first time in two months, we kissed.

It was slow. Ardent. Breathtaking. Her arms were wrapped around me, clutching me tightly as I zestfully ran my fingers through her thin brown hair. Our hearts were pounding. Our bodies were one as we rediscovered each other's lips, wrestled each other's tongues, leapt into each other's mouths. When we finally pulled away, we gazed into each other's eyes with giddy smiles on our faces, and in that moment, I remember thinking that everything was right with the world. I remember thinking that it had all been worth it: all the fighting, all the angst, all the despair—even the disruption to my degree and my novel––because it had all turned out so wonderfully in the end. It was New Year's Eve and I was on a balcony overlooking stunning Sydney Harbour, kissing the girl who I was now sure I'd be spending the rest of my life with. I felt spectacular. *Thank-you, God,* I whispered in my head.

But then Brad got furious.

'If you're just going to hook up with Danny all night, then I'm going to leave!'

He stormed away. Chanel went after him.

'Hold on a second, Danny,' she said over her shoulder.

I could see them at the foot of the steps that led to the street. They were talking to one another, and I was making small-talk with someone else, just passing the time until Chanel and I could get back to making out on the balcony. I was fantasising about kissing her on the dot of midnight, seeing in the new year with her wrapped in my arms, and then taking her back to my place so we could celebrate it properly. I thought it was going to be one of those magical nights that we'd never forget, one of those nights we'd one day be telling our kids about: *the time when Mummy and Daddy got back together again . . .*

Those were the thoughts that were dancing through my mind when I saw her kiss Brad.

My jaw dropped. I stared at them, bewildered. Aghast. But on some level I think I always knew.

She saw me gaping at them and quickly jumped up and pulled me inside. Of course I was furious. I accused her of lying to me the whole time.

'No! No!' she protested. 'That was just a drunken mistake! He means nothing to me! *You're* the one I want!'

She hooked up with me and then Brad got pissed off, so he pulled her away to talk to her. I sat stewing by myself as all the anguish and the stress and the misery of the last five months came roaring right back before Casey put the nail in the coffin:

'I'm sorry bro, but I just overhead her telling him the same thing that she just told you—that kissing you was a mistake, that you mean nothing to her, and that he's the one she's always wanted.'

The rest of the night was a disaster. As the fireworks brought in 2008, the three of us yelled and screamed at each other in the middle of the street while a bunch of our friends watched on around us.

'You always said that Danny was just your friend!' Brad yelled at her. 'You always said that he was obsessed with you but that you never liked him! You always said that no matter how many times you told him it was over he never got the message!'

'What the fuck!' I yelled. 'Chanel, the whole time you were telling *me—*'

'No! No!' she screamed. 'Both of you—just settle down! Brad, let me talk to you for a moment. Danny, don't go anywhere—I want to talk to you afterwards.'

By then it was obvious she'd been leading a double life, particularly since she kept trying to separate Brad and me like so to avoid us comparing stories. On one such occasion I remembered that I had her six day old $1,200 iPhone that had been imported from overseas for Christmas. Chanel had clearly been lying through her teeth, so I decided to read through the messages she'd been sending Brad to try and get closer to the bottom of what'd been going on. Within a minute, I found a text she'd sent him three days earlier.

'You're my soul mate,' it said.

I was infuriated. I'd never been so angry before.

'I feel like smashing this fucking phone,' I told Casey.

'Do it,' he said.

'Do it,' the rest of my school mates said.

I'd been drinking for the past 12 hours—nearly half a case of beer, the first bottle of bourbon, and a good portion of the second bottle of bourbon—not to mention that I'd also smoked one or two joints. I was overwhelmingly pissed off and my judgement was not what it usually was.

So I smashed it to pieces.

Eventually, Chanel and Brad went their separate ways, and that was the end of it. I stayed at the party, furious and heartbroken. My worst fears had come true: *Chanel and Brad were never "just friends". She was playing me the whole time. I loved her with all my heart but she never gave a damn.*

My mates did their best to comfort me, but there really wasn't a whole lot they could do. Eventually, I decided to take a cab home. As I waited on the side of the street, I found myself feeling so overwhelmed, so horrifically distraught that I collapsed by the gutter. I started coughing up bile, began trembling uncontrollably, and in that moment, I couldn't see how I'd ever recover from such a devastating experience.

January, 2008

I was racked with grief. There was just so much emotion bottled up inside me. I was irate at the fact that I was always being lied to, and by the way that I'd been so ruthlessly betrayed. I was embarrassed by the way she'd played me in front of everyone. And above all, I was heartbroken that I was all alone after I thought I'd found "the one". I'd never been so shattered before. Never been so devastated. It was the worst time of my life.

On the other hand, I knew I needed to move on. I was at a crossroads—I could either collapse and fall apart or pull myself together and get on with my life—and I knew I needed to do the latter.

I can't change what happened in the past, I told myself, *but I can control what I do from this point forward. And what I need to do now is forget about everything that happened last year and channel all my energy into achieving my goals. I need to work my ass off to get* Chrysalis *finished, and once uni starts I need to study really hard so that I can keep on top of things this time and get a High Distinction average. Last New Year's Eve was a mess, but if I work hard this year then I can spend the next one celebrating getting great marks at uni and publishing my novel. That's the right way to respond to this—by achieving my goals. If I achieve my goals then I'll be happy again, just like I was when I started uni.*

February, 2008

There was still a lot of anger festering inside me, but I tried my best to forget about Chanel and get on with my life. It was hard to write with a clear head, but I managed to do OK. I edited *Chrysalis* to the point where I thought it was ready to be published, and then decided to get it professionally critiqued just to make sure. I caught a break and was lucky enough to be put in touch with Nick Bleszynski through the New South Wales Writers' Centre, an author who's written three bestsellers and mentored two writers who ended up signing major publishing deals.

Once he's read my manuscript, I'll make the changes he suggests and then submit it for publication, I thought.

I figured that after that I'd then be able to switch my attention to my degree, and I was confident that without my novel to worry about I'd be able to study as much as I needed to in order to get a High Distinction average.

~~~

In February, I also decided to spend my savings going to South America at the end of the year to volunteer at an underprivileged school in Cusco, Peru. I found out about the opportunity from a friend, but it was Mr Williams' words at the scholarship dinner the previous year that made me want to do it:

'You've been blessed with so much,' he'd said. 'You've been brought up in a wonderful neighbourhood; you're surrounded by a loving, supportive family; and you've got the opportunity and the ability to do anything you want to in life. I hope you always use your blessings for good. I hope you always do charity work, and I hope you always try to help people. Remember, Danny: to whom much is given, much is expected.'

He's right, I thought. *Even though I'm going through a rough patch right now, I am a very lucky person. I do have a terrific life. And it's my responsibility to start giving back, and lend a helping hand to those less fortunate than myself.*

March, 2008

I did *not* rape her.

But that's what I started hearing when I got back to uni.

'To justify her intimacy with you to Brad, she said that you'd force yourself on her. She said that she wouldn't want you to but that you wouldn't take no for an answer.'

I couldn't believe it. I seriously couldn't believe it. I cherished that girl every day we were together. I treated her like a queen. I would've turned the world upside down to make her happy. So to have her accuse me of something as vile and despicable as rape made me sick to my stomach. It made me so fucking angry.

It made me so fucking angry that I wanted to kill her.

I'm not just saying this—I literally wanted to kill her.

I never, ever actually would've done it. I strongly believe the best revenge in those cases is simply living well. I knew that the right way of responding to everything she'd put me through was to channel my fury into achieving my goals and then go on to live a happy life. I did know that, and that's what I was focused on doing. But after I heard those allegations . . . I'd be lying to you if I said I never got the urge to pick up a baseball bat and smash in her face. I was that enraged.

I mean, lying to me throughout our whole relationship was bad enough.

Two-timing with one of my best friends was even worse.

But saying that I raped her to explain our intimacy?

I don't even know what you call betrayal that extreme.

And being a self-confessed mamma's boy and someone who's always held women in the highest esteem and regard, there's not a more repulsive, heinous act anyone could have possibly accused me of.

April, 2008

I was still finding it so hard to deal with—the heartbreak, the hatred, and most recently my complete and utter disgust at the rape accusations. But what had begun to really tear me up the most was the impact it was all having on my ability to achieve my goals. Half the time I'd be too distraught to study or write properly, so I'd end up barely absorbing anything in lectures or writing crap that I'd later have to toss in the garbage. And as a result, it started happening all over again: I wasn't getting much quality writing done and I'd fallen way behind at uni. So I didn't do well—I didn't get High Distinctions—and the other scholarship holders did, and then I felt so hopeless, felt so inadequate, felt like such a failure again. And I hated that feeling so fucking much. Like I've said, I wanted to be the best. I wanted to be the guy that everyone looked up to. So the fact that I wasn't at the top of the cohort made me overwhelmingly upset with myself.

I need to stop being such a fucking pussy! I'd yell in my head. *I need to pull myself together. Everything with Chanel ended four months ago! There's no way it should still be bothering me now!*

But it did. And the more it bothered me, the more I failed. And the more I failed, the worse I felt.

~~~

Dear Danny,

*Below is my assessment of your work. On the plus side, I think your story has potential—it has a clear plot and the power to be inspirational. However, you have **a lot** of work to do in order to bring your manuscript up to a publishable standard.*

Nick then went on to detail the problems with the draft: *"the writing style is terrible—way too many clichéd similes, unnecessary big words, awkwardly worded sentences, melodramatic scenes and too much repetition"*. It was *"very poorly researched—the kryptonite for any work of historical fiction"*. I had the Caucasian male protagonist fall in love with a coloured girl, a development which had to be *"deeply rethought"*, since *"the racial aspect of the novel isn't dealt with well at all, nor is her love with the protagonist believable—they don't share nearly enough experiences for them to fall in love"*. The motifs I'd employed were *"amateurish"*. The poetry I'd written and inserted here and there was *"awful"*. My use of punctuation was *"neither proper nor effective"*. The ending was *"contrived"*. Nick then offered suggestions for improvement and noted that it takes a long time to write a book of publishable quality, but that I could get there in the end if I worked really hard.

I read through it several times until words like *"terrible"*, *"poor"*, *"amateurish"*, *"contrived"* and *"awful"* began to sink in and I grew furious with myself.

For fuck's sake! I thought. *How did I think this was going to be so easy—waking up one day and deciding to write a novel? No training, no practice, nothing—just waking up one day and deciding to write a novel and thinking I can have it done and dusted in a year writing it part-time. That's ridiculous. That's insane. What the fuck is wrong with me? How the fuck could I be so stupid? How the fuck could I be so naïve? I've failed again. Again. Again and again and again.*

June, 2008

Adolescents need to be educated about depression.

In my humble opinion, they need to be educated about depression in school, and they also need to be educated about depression at home—in the same way they're educated about safe sex and drink driving.

Adolescents need to be educated about depression so that if they find themselves experiencing the symptoms, they can realise that they're suffering from an illness, and can then go about seeking treatment from there.

But if they don't know what depression is?

Then they won't seek help, and will thus prolong their suffering.

Just like my main character Jimmy does in *I Will Not Kill Myself, Olivia*, they might self-medicate with drugs and alcohol and develop an addiction—which, it should be noted, significantly exacerbates depression, since alcohol and some drugs are, of course, depressants.

They might self-medicate with sex, and thereby vastly increase the risk of unwanted pregnancies and STDs.

Like Jimmy also does, they might self-harm.

And worst of all, they might kill themselves.

Some parents think that depression is taboo—something that shouldn't be talked about; something that's too dark for their teenager to be exposed to. If you do think like that, then let me give you some stats:

At the time of writing, in the US, the UK and Australia, as many as 20% of teens will experience depression before they reach adulthood.

Measuring rates of self-harm has proved difficult for a variety of reasons, but there have been studies that estimate that 6-7% of 15-24 year olds intentionally hurt themselves, and other studies that suggest the figures are as high as 12-20%.

For youths aged 15-24, suicide is the third leading cause of death in America.

For the same age group, it is the second leading cause of death in the UK.

And for the same age group in Australia, it is *the* leading cause.

Depression is persecuting youths all over the globe. It's a worldwide epidemic that's everywhere you turn—even if you don't know it, even if the sufferer themself doesn't know it. Regardless of age, gender, sexuality, religion, colour or creed, teens are at risk for a myriad of reasons. Isn't it best that they're educated to spot the warning signs if they do fall victim?

In my opinion, not educating an adolescent about depression because it's too "dark" for their "innocent" mind is nearly as dangerous as not teaching them safe sex because it encourages fornication. I once met a girl who'd been raised like that. After a few drinks at a bar we went back to her place, and she wanted to do it without protection. That shit isn't safe.

The reason I bring all this up is because when I was 19, I couldn't have known any less about depression. I knew what I was feeling—I knew I was in pain—but I had no idea I was starting to develop an illness. If I did I would've gotten the help I needed, and this story would probably end right here.

Alas, it continues . . .

After that semester's exams were finished, I found myself in a seedy motel room in Kings Cross, 25 standard drinks in. My friends were across the room talking amongst themselves, but I was slouched against the wall completely zoned out and still drinking, drinking. Despair tugged at my soul. I felt so overwhelmed. *How am I ever going to work my way out of this mess?* I thought desperately. *I try so hard, but it's never enough. Whenever I study hard enough to get the marks that I want to get, I hardly get any writing done. Whenever I write more, I fall behind at uni. I feel so* inadequate. *All the other scholarship holders are doing such amazing things with their lives—travelling the world, founding charities, interning at the United Nations, or representing the country in sport or debating or who knows what else. And then there's me: getting marks way below my potential and writing books that are so bad they practically need to be rewritten. I feel like such a loser. No matter what I do I can't achieve my goals. It's so frustrating, so disappointing. I feel so unhappy. And I didn't rape her! I did not rape her!*

And this is where it's all led me: to a seedy motel room where I'm still drinking, drinking. And I can't stop. I can't stop. I just can't stop.

July, 2008

I kept fucking up at uni—my average was only 76% that semester—and *Chrysalis* was nowhere near finished. I always felt like such a failure, and that made me always feel miserable. And because I was always miserable, I was always drunk. It had gone way beyond the point of what's socially acceptable. Every time I went out I'd plough through 20 or 30 standard drinks and end up losing control of myself. It got to the stage where my friends were pissed off with me, and the ones that weren't were worried. I just couldn't stay sober. If I had one drink then I'd end up having another and then another and then another and then before I knew it I'd had 25 and was a complete and utter mess.

One of my mates told me that he'd started to drink a lot less so that he could be in a better position to look after me when I inevitably needed him to. That was a wake-up call that something had to change. Craving booze in the middle of the day, that was another wake-up call. Standing still while some punk kept punching me in the face outside Star City and being too drunk to feel it—that was another wake-up call that I really needed to stop drinking.

After I admitted I had a problem to myself, I then admitted it to my parents. They were really understanding, as I knew they would be.

'We're not here to pass judgment on you, Danny. We're your parents. We love you, and we just want to do whatever it takes to help you get better.'

We talked for a long time, and I agreed to see a psychologist who specialised in treating people with an addiction.

~~~

For the third time that week I found myself on the edge of my bed, sweating, clutching my hair, panting through gritted teeth. I wanted booze so badly. My whole body was begging for it. Like I say in *I Will Not Kill Myself, Olivia*, craving a substance is like being really, really hungry, and fighting it is like not eating. It's wholly consuming. There's nothing else you can think about, nothing else you can do until it has mercy on you and passes. But seeing the psychologist had been helpful, and I tried to use some of the techniques she'd taught me as I kept panting, kept sweating, kept ripping strands of hair out of my head:

Just hold off drinking for the next hour, I told myself. It's what I'd told myself an hour beforehand, and it's what I'd have to keep telling myself to get through the night. The idea was to break down a seemingly insurmountable task into a number of surmountable ones. Simple I know, but it worked.

Just hold off drinking for the next hour . . . I'd murmur. *It's only an hour . . . it's only an hour . . . you did it last hour so you can do it this hour, too. Just stay strong . . . keep fighting . . . don't give in. No matter how much you want to you cannot give in . . .*

August, 2008

By the end of the mid-year holidays I felt so much better. It'd been five weeks since I'd touched alcohol and the cravings were gone, and with the passing of time, my anger towards Chanel had begun to fade. For the first time in months my mind felt clear—I was able to wake up and just write, write, write. It was so enjoyable, and over the previous couple of weeks I'd gotten so much done. It was just great to be able to live freely again, instead of always floundering.

Finally, I thought, *all of the drama is behind me—all the shit with Chanel, and the alcoholism, and the misery. And now that it is, I'm ready to throw myself into clocking up a High Distinction average and getting my novel published by the end of the year. I'm going to smash it! I can't wait for the next semester to start!*

PART II

OR

IT'S REALLY HARD TO GET BETTER IF YOU DON'T GET HELP

September, 2008

In *I Will Not Kill Myself, Olivia*, Jimmy's girlfriend is called, as the title suggests, Olivia. They were high school sweethearts and on their way to the altar, but then for reasons that don't need to be dealt with here, Jimmy falls victim to a crippling depression. From that point on in the novel I start exploring what can happen to a couple when they become a threesome: i.e. the man, the woman, and the serious mental illness.

What sort of chaos can it lead to?

How does it change the relationship? Does it bring both of them closer together or does it rip them apart?

Is the healthy partner's love and support enough to get the depressed partner through it, or does he/she still need to receive professional treatment?

And, even if the depressed partner does get better, will their relationship ever be the same?

I never had a girlfriend throughout my war with depression like Jimmy did, but I did have a close friend called Sylvia, who if truth be told, was the inspiration for Olivia herself. The two situations were hardly the same—Jimmy and Olivia were ardent lovers who wanted to spend their lives together, whereas Sylvia and I were friends living on opposite sides of the globe. Nevertheless, we often used to reach out to each other for advice and support, and some of the relationship-related questions I explore in my novel were based on real life events that happened between Sylvia and myself.

And so, she enters this story with a Facebook message:

Hey Sylvia,

I thought I was better. I honestly thought I'd beaten it. But somehow I've fallen right back into that state of almost permanent despair. Striking the right balance between studying and writing has trumped me again. It's only been six weeks and I've already fallen behind at uni and progress on my novel is slow. I feel like such a fucking idiot. How did I think this semester would be any different from the last ones? Every semester I've had at uni has been a failure, and I'm well on my way to failing this one too. I hate this. And I hate myself for making it like this.

As usual, my solution is to work harder. I think if I could study and write for a total of 60 hours a week, then I should be able to achieve my goals. I think working 60 hours a week would allow me to get a lot of work done and still give me plenty of time to tutor high school kids, coach basketball, play basketball, go to the gym, and go out with my friends. Then again, maybe 60 hours a week isn't enough either. Maybe I need to be pushing myself harder. Maybe I should be working 70 hours a week. Maybe 80. Maybe more. I'm going to feel miserable until my novel's published and I've achieved a High Distinction average, so maybe I shouldn't be doing anything else apart from studying and writing. Fucking hell . . . I don't know. I just feel so overwhelmed. Everything seems so hopeless. I've lost so much confidence. So much of my self-belief has disappeared. I never thought I'd say this, but I don't know if I can achieve my goals anymore.

I hope you can say something to help, Sylvia. I'm really struggling at the moment and could use your support.

Love,

Danny.

She replied a few days later:

Hey Danny,

I'm so sorry to hear that you're hurting again. I know it must be hard being so unhappy and feeling like you can't achieve your goals, but whatever you do, just keep hanging in there. You've faced some really hard challenges before and you've always overcome them, and I *know you're going to do the same here too. Remember back in high school, when you never used to study and all you cared about was basketball? You were so devastated when you injured your knee and you had no shot at going pro anymore—and because you were in the bottom 20 out of 160 students everyone said you were dumb and would amount to nothing—but you turned your life around and finished school in the top 0.4% of the state. I've always found your ability to overcome setbacks really inspiring, and I know you're going to overcome this too. You're one of the strongest people I know, Danny. Seriously—I've never met anyone with the kind of will power and determination you have. So remember that, and know that it will let you achieve what you want. It always has.*

But at the same time, it might be a good idea to try and not be so hard on yourself all the time. Seriously, Danny—you always put so much pressure on yourself to achieve such difficult goals, and that's really what seems to be making you so unhappy. I mean, if you get an average of 75- or 80% instead of 85%, is it really the end of the world? Those marks are still really good by almost anyone's standards! And what about your book? Does it really matter if you finish it and get it published this year or the next? Either way you'll have written and published a book, right? That's incredible! How many other 19 year olds can say that?

But aside from that, Danny, just keep at it. Keep believing in yourself, keep having faith in God, and know that I believe in you too. You can do this—I know you can. So just keep working hard and soon you'll get your High Distinction average and be a published author.

Love always,
Sylvia.

In the same way Olivia does for Jimmy, Sylvia had a way of filling me with hope. Having her say that she believed in me meant the world, because as I've intimated, I wasn't someone who was used to being believed in. My family were great and had faith in me no matter what, but aside from them I was always being doubted. There was everything that happened after I busted my knee, but even after I did do well in school, when I told the same people I was going to write a novel, they laughed at me again.

'You've got to be joking!' they all said. 'You're only good at "maths" subjects. English was your worst by far. You can't write. You struggled with *essays*, for crying out loud! How do you, of all people, think you can possibly get a novel published?'

I'm going to do it because I have the right attitude to succeed, I'd think. *I have a tireless work ethic and relentless determination, and I never, ever, ever give up. That's how I managed to overcome my knee injury and succeed in school, and it's also how I'm going to get my novel published. With the attitude I have, anything is possible, and even though I may struggle and fall, I'll get up every time and get what I'm going for in the end.*

But aside from my family, Sylvia was the only one who saw that, which is why I cherished her belief in me so much. In fact, I treasured it even more than my family's faith in me, for the same reason that it means more to a teenage girl when the football captain says she's beautiful than when she hears it from her father. Having Sylvia say that she had confidence in me and that I had what it took to achieve my goals always gave me hope that everything would turn out well in the end. It gave me strength. It inspired me. And when I felt hopeful, strong and inspired, I stopped feeling depressed.

I didn't agree with what Sylvia said at the end of her message, though—that it didn't really matter if I only got 80% instead of 85% or if *Chrysalis* got published later than I hoped.

I need to be at the top of the cohort, I thought. *I need to be the best. And 80% is not the best. A few of the other scholarship holders get High Distinction averages, so that means that I have to get a High Distinction average. Anything less is unacceptable. Anything less is a failure. And I need to finish* Chrysalis *this year and get it published as soon as possible because as much as I enjoy writing it, it is a huge disruption to my degree, and getting a High Distinction average would be a whole lot easier if I wasn't writing a novel at the same time.*

So I was convinced that Sylvia wasn't right on that front. Instead, I thought the solution was to just work harder: *if I can work for a total of 60 hours a week, then I should be able to achieve my goals and then everything will be fine.*

October, 2008

Life is such a fight. Such an all-out slog. I work so hard. I drive myself to exhaustion. But no matter how much I try I keep on sinking. Every week I fall further behind at uni, and progress on Chrysalis *is far from good. It's just too much. It's all just too much. Every week I feel under more and more pressure, I feel more and more suffocated, so much so that the fun's been sucked out of everything. I get no pleasure out of life anymore. Nothing exists for me except despair. And the worst part is that at times, I can't see myself ever waking up from this nightmare. At times there's nothing to indicate I'm ever going to get better. And when I feel that hopeless, I start craving booze. I just want to lock myself in my room with that litre bottle of Beam and sit on the floor and drink and drink and drink until I eventually pass out. And when I feel like that, I can't study properly, I can't write properly . . . and then I feel even more miserable, and then I want to drink even more, and then I'm even more useless, and then I get even more unhappy, I get even more overwhelmed. I mean what the fuck am I supposed to do? I'm already trying my best. I'm already running myself into the ground. And it's never enough. It's never enough. So what the fuck am I supposed to do?*

~~~

I'm fucking hopeless. I'm fucking pathetic. I'm such a lazy fucking piece of shit. Who the fuck can't work 60 hours a week to achieve their goals? It doesn't matter how exhausted I am. It doesn't matter how dreadful I feel. Only working 54 hours this week is a fucking disgrace. That's fucking pathetic. I'm such a fucking slacker. I should be ashamed of myself I'm so fucking lazy.

~~~

Sylvia,

I'm cracking, I'm breaking at the seams. I work so hard to try and keep it together but no matter what I do it's never enough. I just keep getting more and more miserable. I know I'm going to hang in there, I know I'm going to keep on fighting, because that's who I am, that's all I know how to do—but right now it all seems to be in vain. I just can't see how I'm going to achieve my goals, and so I can't see how I'm ever going to be happy. And somehow even after all these months, I still have so much fucking anger pent up towards Chanel.

Put it all together and I'm desperate to drink. The cravings are insatiable. I try to fight through them but they won't go away. They just keep growing, more and more intense. So I thought I'd Facebook you. It was either that or drowning myself in booze.

Please say something, anything to help.

Love,

Danny.

~~~

For the third night that week I found myself on the edge of the bed dripping with sweat, gripping my hair, gasping through gritted teeth in desperation for the bottle. I was so miserable. So overwhelmed. I just wanted to forget everything, just wanted to escape but I knew it wasn't right. So once again I retrieved Sylvia's Facebook message from my pocket—the one she'd sent me in response to my previous one when I was feeling that way and begging her for help. I read it through, one, two, three times, and then I kept rereading the part where she said that I was strong and that she believed in me and that everything would turn out well in the end. I was clutching it so tightly that it was crumpling, that it was getting tattered and frayed in my frenzied grasp, but as I kept reading it, hope gradually breathed back into me, and the clenching, the sweating, the panting finally came to a halt.

As it always did, hearing Sylvia say that she had faith in me strengthened my resolve. It gave me confidence when I needed it most.

She's right, I eventually concluded. *I am strong, and I can achieve my goals if I keep working hard. I'm behind the 8-ball at the moment, but the mid-semester break's coming up next week and I can catch up then. So I'm going to be OK. I'll work really hard and then everything's going to turn out well.*

And now that I was feeling refortified, I didn't feel the need to drink. I folded up Sylvia's message, put it back in my pocket, and stood at the foot of my bed to do my prayers:

> *Dear God,*
>   *Thank-you for blessing me with food, shelter, my family, and the opportunity and the ability to pursue my dreams.*
>   *I pray for everybody who is suffering right now, and I pray that you take care of them—just as well as you take care of me.*

I paused for a moment, recalling all the loving, kind, inspiring things Sylvia had said in her message as I became flushed with gratitude.

> *And I thank you for blessing me with Sylvia's compassion. I thank you for bestowing me with such a caring friend.*
>   *I love You, God.*
>   *Amen.*

I then turned out the light and crawled into bed to try and catch a couple of hours sleep before class the next day.

~~~

What the fuck is wrong with me? I tell myself I'm a hard worker, I tell myself I have the discipline to achieve my goals, but then this week I only manage to work 53 hours? There are no excuses—that's fucking atrocious. That's a fucking disgrace. I'm such a fucking slacker. Such a worthless fucking piece of shit.

Enough. This cannot happen anymore. This is fucking ridiculous, and it can never happen ever again. Never, ever, ever again.

So I came up with a plan to make me work harder:

I'm going to start cutting myself.

Starting just above the wrist, I'm going to cut myself with a steak knife every time I don't work 60 hours a week. It makes sense. When I do something wrong, it's my fault. And if it's my fault, then I deserve to be punished. So whenever I don't work hard enough so that I fall behind at uni or don't get as much of my novel written as I need to, I'm going to cut myself. Maybe if I do this I won't be so lazy. Maybe if I do this I won't fail so much.

I never actually ended up harming myself, but it's a testament to my rapidly deteriorating mental health that doing so seemed completely normal to me. That's what depression does—it bends straight lines, complicates simple equations. But because I'd never been educated about it, I still didn't know I was depressed. I thought I was just going through a rough patch—I had no idea I was suffering from an illness. So instead of getting the help I needed, I just continued spiralling further and further downwards.

~~~

The following week, I snapped. I broke my three month sober stretch. Drank a bottle of bourbon alone in my room. Even Sylvia's message couldn't save me then. The anxiousness, the misery, the pressure, how overwhelmed I felt . . . it became unbearable. I was desperate for an escape and I didn't care how I got it.

~~~

I remember my first fantasy about death like it was yesterday. It was four in the morning, and I was cramming for a stats exam I was way behind on.

'You're gonna fail, you're gonna fail,' whispered a voice in my head.

'You're gonna fail, you're gonna fail.'

I tried to push it to the side, I tried to forget about it, but no matter what I did it was always there, heckling me, taunting me.

'You're so far behind. You'll never catch up. You're going to fail. Again. Just like you always do.'

It fed my fear, heightened it, made me want to scream.

'You're gonna fail, you're gonna fail.'

I need an escape, I thought. *Relief from the ceaseless dread.*

'You're gonna fail, you're gonna fail.'

Need booze. Fucking gagging for it.

'You're gonna fail, you're gonna fail.'

Shut up! Shut the fuck up!

'You're gonna fail, you're gonna fail.'

I want to die! I just want to die!

I hate my life so much that I just want to die!

At that point, the "low battery" notification flashed across the screen of my laptop:

Only 10% remaining. Connect to a power source immediately.

I retrieved the charger from my bag, and as I was about to plug it in to the power point, I remember hoping that something would go wrong—that there'd be some sort of technical malfunction—so that when I plugged in the chord I'd be electrocuted to death.

And I remember feeling dejected that I wasn't. I remember feeling disappointed that I was still breathing in a world I no longer wanted to be a part of.

November, 2008

I hardly slept during the exam week that semester. I had to study round the clock to try and catch up, and even then I was still badly prepared, having to resort to learning coursework on the day of the exam. I felt so burnt out, so horribly drained, like a horse that'd been flogged to the point of death. And on the night of my last exam, as I tried to fight off the fear of failure that had been progressively engulfing me; as I tried to swallow down the sick feeling lodged deep in my throat; as I ran to the bathroom thinking I was going to puke; as I coughed and spluttered up bile in the sink; and as I stared into the mirror at my black-rimmed eyes that were puffing out from my exhausted, unshaven, sorrowful face, I knew that something had to change. Studying Commerce/Law full-time, writing a novel, tutoring high school students, coaching basketball, playing basketball, going to the gym—it was too much. I realised I was going to self-destruct if I kept going like that.

~~~

My average was 74% that semester, and my novel was still nowhere near finished. I talked over what I could do with my parents, and after we'd analysed each option to death, we all agreed that the best thing for me to do would be to ease my workload the following year by only doing one subject a semester instead of four. I figured having effectively a year off uni would give me time to finish my novel and get it published, after which I could come back refreshed, and with my writing done and dusted, I'd have enough time to keep on top of my subjects and get a High Distinction average. I hated the fact that it had come to this. I hated the fact that I was delaying my corporate career a year. I hated the fact that I was falling behind the rest of the scholarship students. But I knew it was just something I had to do. It was, as they say, the lesser of two evils.

December, 2008

The days were better after uni was finished, because I didn't have to worry about studying—but I was still far from happy. Two years beforehand, happiness and I were bundled together, but since then it'd been kind of like the Big Bang, myself and happiness stretching further and further apart until it seemed like nothing more than a dim pinprick in the great blackness of space. It felt like I had no sun. In my world it was always winter. I tried to write but my mind was too hazy. I had the focus of a bored child.

A vivid memory I have of that time is being on my flight to Chile. Before I left, everyone was saying that I'd have the time of my life. But whenever I thought about it, I just couldn't see how. I just couldn't fathom the concept of enjoying myself. In my dismal state, the idea of pleasure seemed too foreign. Too farfetched. And in those silent, pensive hours, when the lights were switched off and the whole plane was asleep except for me, my thoughts kept returning to the same lone question:

Will I ever be happy, again?

And also to the same answer:

I don't know.

I really, genuinely, truthfully don't know.

Santiago, Chile – New Year's Eve, 2008

I was plastered for the second time in three days. I knew I shouldn't have been drinking, given my history with alcoholism, but I didn't care. I was finally enjoying myself, and I didn't care. I was sick of being unhappy and I was prepared to do anything to feel good again.

'Hey Danny, do you want to snort some coke?' a bloke at the hostel asked.

'Never had it before, bro. What's it like?'

'Oh it's so good, man. It makes you feel so alive. It makes you feel on top of the world. Two snorts and you'll be flying, man.'

I just wanted to be happy. I'd been miserable all year and I just wanted to feel happy again.

'Yeah, let's do it, dude.'

So we went to a club and got blazed. We stayed there all night long, dancing, drinking, coking and having the best time I'd had in months before the club closed at five and I had to go back to the hostel and pack so that I could take my 9am flight to Cusco, Peru.

Cusco, Peru – January, 2009

Particularly since Mr Williams had emphasised it, I'd been very mindful of the fact that I'd been tremendously blessed. I was very grateful to have been brought up in a wonderful neighbourhood; to be surrounded by a loving, supportive family; and to have been gifted with the opportunity and the ability to do anything I wanted to in life. I knew that I was a lucky man—but I never knew how lucky until I went to Cusco.

Before I went there, I'd never been to a place where 56% of the population lived on less than US$1 a day, where 85% of children never attended high school, where the school drop-out rate was 40%, where the unemployment rate was 42%, where the underemployment rate was 74%, where the literacy rate was 18%, where the infant mortality rate was 5%, and where the average life expectancy was 41 years.

I'd never met any children who wore the same World Vision clothes to school every day.

I'd never been to a school where not a single kid was fat, nor had I ever been called fat by anyone else, which is what some of the children thought the volunteers were because we weren't bone-skinny.

I'd never had 10 year olds try to sell me cigarettes on the street at two in the morning on a school night to help support their family.

I'd never been too embarrassed to tell someone I had a swimming pool in my backyard, like I was when my host family—who lived in a flat barely larger than my living room—had asked me to describe my home to them.

I'd never lived in a place where only ice-cold water came out of the taps, meaning that I had to heat it with a kettle and use a bucket and cup to shower.

I'd never seen villages of houses that didn't have any windows and were made out of mud bricks, much less had I helped build chimneys out of bamboo for said houses so that smoke wouldn't suffocate the air when the families cooked over a fire.

I'd never been to a place where all the adults looked 20 years older than their actual age, and where people as young as 30 had dry and wrinkled skin.

I'd never met a kid who grabbed other peoples' crotches and stuck his fingers up their bums during a school yard game of dodge ball.

'Why does he do that?' one of the volunteers asked.

'Because . . . he gets sexually abused at home.'

'By who?'

The volunteer manager released a painful sigh.

'By his father.'

We were all flabbergasted.

'How come . . . how come no-one's reported it?'

'We have.'

'And?'

He sighed again.

'The police . . . it's not like in your country. There's so much corruption . . . it's not like in your country.'

'But surely something can be done about it?'

'I'm afraid not.'

Seeing this poverty, this exploitation, this corruption, this perversion; waking up every morning and staring it in the face . . . it can change you. And it certainly changed me. Like I said I was aware of it before, but working in that community made me realise just how immensely privileged I really was. And when I looked into the eyes of those skinny kids wearing World Vision clothes, I knew that it was up to me as one of the extremely fortunate people in this world to step up and give them a helping hand. So I did whatever I could there, whether that was helping to build a chicken coup or a vegetable patch so the children could have eggs and vegies as a constant source of food, helping to build chimneys for the houses in the villages, or working on a new classroom for the school. And as I hammered away, I knew that that wouldn't be the end for me. I knew I wouldn't just go back to Sydney and forget about that place. I knew it was the start of something big. In time, I knew that I was going to be making a much bigger contribution to that community than just pounding nails.

~~~

I was feeling great while I was in Cusco, because I was loving all the volunteer work I'd been doing. But the other reason I'd been enjoying myself so much was because of all the partying. Five nights a week I was hitting the town, drinking until midnight before getting on the marching powder and flying until four. I thought being high on coke was the best feeling in the world. Whenever I took it I felt like I could run forever, fly, conquer the world. I just felt so confident, vivacious and energetic. I felt the exact opposite of depressed. And when I was dancing on top of the bar at three in the morning, fucked out of my mind and fist-pumping like hell to the music, I felt so incredible that it was hard to imagine I ever was.

February, 2009

After six weeks in South America, I went to Auckland, New Zealand for a week-long stopover on the way home and dived back into writing my novel. I'd missed it so, so much, and it was great to return to it after all those weeks. Every morning I'd stroll down to Esquires, order myself a milkshake and a ham and cheese croissant and just write, write, write. Now that I was no longer so stressed out with uni, working on my novel was back to filling me with indescribable joy. I was on a high all week, just from being able to do what I loved. And when I wasn't writing, I was thinking about writing: my characters, plot twists, how it all tied together. And when I wasn't thinking about writing, I was fantasising about getting published. I'd imagine how incredible it would feel, receiving that phone call where I'm offered a contract and falling to the floor with overwhelming happiness, crying deliriously into the palms of my hands. I wanted it more than I'd ever wanted anything before. I didn't think there was a single thing on earth I wouldn't do—aside from hurting someone else or violating my ethics—to achieve my dream. It was an obsession that dominated my thoughts. There were nights I'd just lie awake, thinking about it, longing for it, aching for it. Even then, I knew that if it happened it would be the best moment of my life.

~~~

I nearly missed my flight because I was passed out drunk and slept through my alarm, but somehow I managed to make it and there I was, flying back home seven weeks later a brand new man. I had an amazing time, and I was so excited to get back to Sydney and start my year of writing. *I can't believe how lucky I am!* I thought. *I mean, I actually get to spend the whole year working on my dream! How amazing is that?* I just felt so happy again. *Gone are the days when I feel worthless, when I feel so overwhelmed that I want to lock myself in my room and drink until I'm numb, when I feel so miserable that I wish I was dead.* My self-esteem, my self-confidence, my exuberance for life was back, and for the first time in a long time, I felt free, like an eagle, wings mended and ready to soar through the sky, chase my dreams, catch them, and live happily ever after.

~~~

On my first weekend back in Sydney, I'd organised to catch up with some of my friends in Darling Harbour. About an hour and a half before my mate Cal was coming to pick me up, I mixed myself a stiff bourbon and cola and continued working on *Chrysalis*. After South America I didn't have much money to spend at the clubs, so I wanted to get as smashed as possible before I went out so I didn't end up sober and have a shocker of a night.

Cal came when he said he would, by which time the litre bottle of Beam was close to finished and I was shitfaced. I went to greet him at the door, stumbling already.

'Sup man?' I yelled.

'Danny . . . are you trashed already?'

'Yeah, bro! Let's go hit the clubs!'

He didn't even look shocked. I was in the same condition when he saw me the previous night too.

We met the other boys at Darling Harbour and decided to go to Cargo Bar. The guys got let in, but when I went to give the bouncer my ID he shook his head.

'You can't come in tonight,' he said.

'Aww, why not man?' I slurred.

'You've had too much to drink.'

'Naahhh, bro. You've gotta let me in!'

He shook his head and told me to leave. My mates tried to talk him into letting me inside but he stood his ground.

'That guy was a fucking cock!' I said loudly as we were walking away. 'Why the fuck didn't he let me in?'

My mates shook their heads.

'Anyway fuck Cargo!' I kept ranting. 'Let's go to Bungers!'

We lined up at Bungalow8 but it was the same story there too. I lined up again and again, hoping that a different bouncer would card me and let me in, but I was refused entry every time. We gave up when they threatened to blacklist me from the club and call the police if I didn't leave.

'Why are all the bouncers being such fucking assholes tonight?' I yelled.

'They're not being fucking assholes,' one of my mates finally said. 'You're wasted as fuck. You shouldn't even be out.'

'Naahhh, man! They're all just being fucking assholes tonight!'

Eventually we got let in to Strike Bar down the road. I headed straight for the bar and started smashing back cocktails.

'Stop drinking, stop drinking,' everyone was telling me.

But I couldn't stop. When some guys go out their entire night's about trying to get laid, but with me it was all about trying to get as much booze into me as possible. Once that switch got flicked I craved it and it became all I could think about.

I was being loud and obnoxious. My friends got more and more pissed off and at some point left without saying goodbye. Cal said he'd take me home, so I stumbled into his car and passed out in the front seat.

He woke me up when we reached my house. I got out of the car and staggered away in the opposite direction. He tried to guide me inside but I broke free and kept lurching away, stumbling and falling in the neighbour's garden. Eventually he gave up and went to get my mum. It was late at night. She answered the doorbell, shocked to see him.

'Cal? What's wrong?' she panicked.

He sighed.

'Hi Mrs Baker. Danny's drunk too much again. Could you please help me get him inside?'

My parents were livid the next day.

'This is disgraceful! What the hell were you thinking! You know you're not supposed to be drinking! You know that if you do you're going to ruin your life!'

I thought about how pissed off my friends were with me. I remembered how completely out of control I'd been. There was no escaping the conclusion: *my parents are right. I can't keep drinking. I have to stop.*

After my parents stopped berating me, I started berating myself.

What the fuck is wrong with me? How the fuck could I let it get to this stage? How the fuck do I not know by now that I can't control myself when I drink? I'm such a fucking idiot. Such a fucking loser. Such a stupid fucking piece of shit.

I was so disgusted with myself for fucking up again. I felt so worthless. I felt like such a failure. And as a result, it was back.

Depression.

Surrounding me, swarming me, throttling me ruthlessly as ever. It was the depression that always came with feeling like a failure, but this time, it was greatly exacerbated by the fact that I'd previously tricked myself into thinking I was healthy again. I thought I'd beaten it, but nothing could've been further from the truth and it scared the shit out of me.

How the hell could I feel so good, feel so certain that I'd conquered my demons, only to feel like this seven days later? It's been a whole year now—how can I still feel so miserable after all these months?

And then came the most terrifying thought that a person with depression can possibly have: *will I always feel this way? Is this just the way I am? Will I forever be condemned to a life of insufferable pain and despair?*

If at the end of the day, all people want is to be happy, then is this feeling—*will I forever be condemned to a life of insufferable pain and despair?*—not the most terrifying feeling we can possibly experience?

As I state in *I Will Not Kill Myself, Olivia*, the fact that it haunts everyone in the throes of a prolonged depression—not to mention that by definition, patients are, to say the least, unhappy—is what makes clinical depression such a horrific illness.

March, 2009

There were days when I felt myself—when I was cheerful, when I was excited to be pursuing my dream, when the future seemed bright and full of promise. But it was like I was walking on a tightrope, where the slightest hit would knock me off and send me spiralling into despair. I was so wildly unstable, smiling one moment but then so angry with myself, so overwhelmed with self-hatred, so distraught the next—and always over the simplest of mishaps: missing the bus, forgetting my wallet at home, being five minutes late to class. It was scary as hell, how volatile I was. And I didn't even have booze to weather the storm. I was sober as a nun, for fuck's sake. I was fighting unarmoured. I'd been trying to read to relax but when you're craving bourbon, reading to relax is like hugging when you're horny. I didn't know how to balance without a bottle. Hell, I didn't know how to balance, period. I was a fucking train wreck, a ticking time bomb, set to explode at the slightest provocation.

~~~

And then one morning, I did.

I had a writing course—"how to develop romantic relationships between characters"—at the NSW Writers' Centre in Rozelle at 10am. I took the 7:46 bus to Queen Victoria Building in the city from the top of my street; it was meant to get there before 9 o'clock, but the peak hour traffic was worse than usual and it didn't arrive until 9:11. I checked the bus time to Rozelle at the stop opposite Town Hall.

Fucking hell, I swore.

The next one left at 9:25.

That's pushing it, I stressed. *That's really fucking pushing it. What if I'm late? What if I miss something really important? What the fuck am I going to do then?*

Wait . . . I finally said to myself. *Just try to relax. Nine twenty-five—I should still be OK. Just calm down. Try not to get so anxious over everything all the time.*

I boarded the bus, reached Rozelle at 9:45. I saw the sign that read "NSW Writers' Centre", so I pressed the button to stop the bus. When I got off I was standing in front of it, but all I could see was a big grassy area and a large complex of buildings.

Where the fuck is this place? I fretted.

I nervously walked through the field, studying all the buildings, but nothing indicated that any of them were the Writers' Centre. With mounting panic I circled them, once, twice, three times, but I still couldn't find where the damn place was.

Then came the self-abuse:

What the fuck have I done? Why the fuck didn't I look up exactly where this place is on a fucking map? Why the fuck didn't I ask for directions? Why the fuck am I so stupid? Why the fuck am I such a fucking moron?

I checked the time on my phone. Three minutes to ten.

Fucking hell! I'm going to be late! I'm going to be late! What the fuck will I do if I'm late?

I let out a loud, desperate groan and ran back to the main road. I looked around hopelessly, but I was lost. I had no idea where I was. Eventually I ran down the street before I saw one perpendicular to the road I was on: Alberto Street. It meant nothing to me. I doubled back through the field and the buildings and hysterically searched for the Writers' Centre but to no avail. I checked the time again: 10:10.

I'm such a cunt! I screamed in my head. *Who the fuck can't get to a fucking course on time! What the fuck is wrong with me? Why the fuck am I so fucking pathetic? Fucking hell! I'm such a cunt, I'm such a cunt, I'm such a cunt!*

I was so angry with myself that I collapsed in a heap beneath a tree and burst into tears. I completely broke down, so overwhelming was my vehement self-loathing, my nauseous distress, my ghastly misery that all I could do was cry and cry and cry. I sat there for what felt like hours just balling my eyes out, and all I could think was, *my life is so fucked up, my life is so fucked up. My life is so fucked up that I wish I was dead.*

Eventually I staggered up, drifted through the streets, tears still streaming down my cheeks. I couldn't think of anything else but death. It's not that I—like most people suffering from severe depression—particularly wanted to die—rather that I was just desperate to escape my harrowing anguish, and death seemed to be the only conceivable way. I imagined how soothing it would be. The answer to all my problems. Just blackness. Gentle, calm, soothing blackness. I fantasised about all the different ways I could do it: slitting my wrists, overdosing, electrocuting myself, poisoning myself, hanging myself, drowning myself, gassing myself . . . and then I saw a bridge, only 50 metres away. I felt a surge of energy and ran towards it.

I felt less overwhelmed the closer I got. To me, the bridge was a salvation, perhaps like what land is to those lost at sea. I felt like I controlled my own destiny again. In a strange way I felt empowered.

I found myself standing at the top of the bridge. I looked down. Instantly I felt a rush of disappointment.

The bridge isn't high enough.

Instead of dying I'll get screwed by luck and just break all my bones.

Racked with grief, I pulled myself away, lurched down the street. I saw a pub and headed straight in.

'What can I get you?' the bartender asked.

I thought about how blissful it would be to taste the bourbon on my lips, to have it pumping through my veins before I melted into numbness. So good. So. Fucking. Good.

'What can I get you?' the bartender repeated.

'Ah . . .'

He raised his eyebrows.

'Um . . . Coke.'

'Just Coke?'

'Yes.'

I can't do it, I finally realised in a moment of strength.

It's not right.

Now's not the time to get drunk. Neither is it time to kill myself. It's the time to sort this mess out. It's the time to face my demons and man up and beat them.

That's the right way to overcome this.

Not by drinking—which will get me into even more trouble.

And definitely not by committing suicide—which is a permanent solution to a temporary problem.

So I sat down at a table with my glass of Coke and called my mum.

'Danny? Why aren't you at the writing course? Is everything all right?'

'No.'

'Why? What happened?'

'Can you . . . can you just come and get me? Please?'

She came. By then I just felt drained. I mumbled what happened on the way home. When we got there, we sat on the dining room couch and talked for a while.

'I can't . . . I can't believe what happened today,' I murmured. 'That whole thing with the bridge . . . I mean that's just . . . that's just *so* screwed up.'

I paused.

'Why am I like this?' I asked. 'What's wrong with me?'

Mum was holding my hand, squeezing it tightly.

'It's going to be OK,' she said. 'Dad, Mathew[3] and I are all here to support you, and tomorrow, we'll go to the doctor and make sure you get the help you need.'

She squeezed my hand even tighter.

'Just keep having faith, Danny. Whatever you do, you can't ever lose hope.'

---

[3] My brother, who's three years younger than me.

~~~

The next day, I saw my general practitioner Dr Kramenin and told him everything. He responded by saying that I was showing classic signs of clinical depression.

I remember being confused. I remember not really getting it.

'Clinical depression?' I asked. 'What do you mean?'

'Clinical depression,' he repeated. 'It's an illness, Danny.'

I still didn't get it.

'What is it, exactly?'

'In lay man's terms, it's basically an intense state of unhappiness, experienced over a prolonged period of time.'

'But . . . but doesn't everyone feel unhappy from time to time?'

'From time to time, yes. But not for prolonged periods. People with depression feel constantly miserable, almost without relief. And the intensity of their despair is usually far greater than that experienced by a non-depressed person. Some people with clinical depression hate themselves. Some self-harm. Some kill themselves. Clinical depression is an illness, Danny, and it can be very serious.'

I nodded. The description fitted like a glove.

'So you think I've got clinical depression, then?'

Dr Kramenin filed through his drawer before handing me a checklist called SPHERE, a scale he said was developed to increase the identification rate of mental illnesses like depression. I started reading it:

For more than TWO WEEKS have you:

Felt sad, down or miserable most of the time?
OR
Lost interest or pleasure in most of your usual activities?

If you answered "YES" to either of these questions, complete the symptom checklist below by circling the symptoms that are applicable to you:

Behaviours

Stopped going out;

Not getting things done at work;

Withdrawn from close family and friends;

Relying on alcohol and sedatives;

Stopped doing things you enjoy;

Unable to concentrate.

Thoughts

"I'm a failure";

"It's my fault";

"Nothing good ever happens to me";

"I'm worthless";

"Life is not worth living".

Feelings

Overwhelmed;

Unhappy, depressed;

Irritable;

Frustrated;

No confidence;

Guilty;

Indecisive;

Disappointed;

Miserable;

Sad.

Physical

Tired all the time;

Sick and run down;

Headaches and muscle pains;

Churning gut;

Can't sleep;

Poor appetite/weight loss.

I answered "yes" to "in the last two weeks have you felt sad, down or miserable most of the time" and then circled "relying on alcohol and sedatives", "unable to concentrate", "I'm a failure", "I'm worthless", "it's my fault", "overwhelmed", "unhappy, depressed", "guilty", "disappointed", "frustrated", "miserable", "sad", "irritable" and "life is not worth living". After I was finished, I handed the test back to Dr Kramenin.

'You circled 14 symptoms,' he said. 'According to the authors of the test, you are likely to have a depressive illness if you circled at least three.'

Dr Kramenin then asked me a few additional questions, like whether I was also experiencing periods of mania or whether I'd had any hallucinations, for the purpose of ruling out whether I was exhibiting symptoms of other mental illnesses like bipolar disorder or schizophrenia. After being satisfied that I wasn't, he concluded that I was in fact suffering from depression.

'What . . . what do I do?' I asked concernedly.

'I'm going to place you on an antidepressant medication,' he said.

Once again I was confused.

'Medication? For depression? How can that be?'

'If you have depression, then it means you have a chemical imbalance in your brain—a deficiency of either serotonin, dopamine, adrenalin or noradrenalin. We use medication to treat depression in the same way we use medication to treat physical illnesses. There's no difference, really.'

I was shocked. I'd never heard of such a thing before. Then again like I've said, I hadn't heard of clinical depression before, either.

'I'm going to place you on a selective serotonin reuptake inhibitor,' he continued. 'This SSRI will increase the amount of serotonin in your brain, and thereby work to correct this chemical imbalance. You should feel better after that.'

He gave me a sample packet of pills and a prescription for more when the sample ran out.

April, 2009

I feel so much better! Ever since I started taking antidepressants a couple of weeks ago my brain has felt a hundred times clearer! My suicidal thoughts have vanished, and every day is so much easier without that voice in my head telling me that I'm a loser and a fuck up and a failure. I actually feel healthy again—probably as healthy as I've felt since back in 2007 before my symptoms began making their way to the fore. I'm so stoked! I know I've said this a hundred times before, but I really think I'm cured! I think I'm finally cured this time! All I needed was antidepressants! Now all my problems are solved and I can get on with writing my novel and trying to get it published by the end of the year!

The fact that I thought I'd beaten it once again just goes to show how little I knew about depression. While medication can be very helpful, unfortunately recovery isn't as simple as just popping a pill.

May, 2009

Hey Sylvia,

I'm so depressed again. I have no idea how. I've been taking my meds, but I think they've stopped working or something. So what am I supposed to do? How am I supposed to beat this illness? I keep thinking I've beaten it but I never have. I feel like I have no control over my brain. I feel crazy.

I'm becoming such a recluse. I don't want to talk to my friends anymore, because I don't think I'll have anything non-depressing to say. So don't worry about replying to this message or my last one. You must hate having to keep hearing about my problems all the time, so I'm going to stop dumping them on you and just leave you alone. You're better off without me, anyway.

Danny.

She replied that same day:

Oh my God Danny please don't think that you're dumping all your problems on me or that I'd be better off without you! Seriously, nothing could be further from the truth! I want to be here for you whenever I can because you're my friend, Danny—I care about you so much and I want you to keep telling me about what you're going through so that I can try to help if I can. So please don't ever forget that. Seriously—thinking that you're dumping all your problems on me or that I'm better off without you is absolutely ridiculous! You're my friend and I'm here to support you and that's all there is to it.

That being said, Danny, I'm not a psychologist, and I really think you need to start seeing one. I am only about to finish my *second year of Psychology at uni, but one thing my professors have really hammered into me is that just taking the drugs won't necessarily fix everything . . . or anything. The aim of medication is to treat the symptoms you're feeling, whereas therapy aims to deal with the underlying causes as well as the symptoms. Sometimes the reason people are depressed is because of the way they think about one or more aspects of their life, but with Cognitive Behavioural Therapy, you can actually learn to rewire the way you think and thus make yourself look at things in a way that doesn't make you feel so depressed. I know your mum has been telling you to see a psychologist too, so I think you should definitely do it. Maybe then you can conquer your depression for good and stop having so many relapses.*

Apart from that, Danny, just keep hanging in there. You're so strong, you can get through this. Just keep fighting and you'll beat it in the end. I know you will.

Love always,

Sylvia.

~~~

In light of everything my mum and Sylvia were telling me, I scheduled another appointment to see Dr Kramenin.

'Do you think I need to see a psychologist?' I asked. 'I've heard they can be really helpful—that sometimes the reason you're depressed is because of the way you think about certain aspects of your life, and that therapy can, among other things, rewire the way you think so that you can look at things in a way that doesn't make you feel depressed. What do you think? Would it be a good idea for me to see one?'

Dr Kramenin shrugged his shoulders.

'Danny, the reason that *you're* depressed is because of your situation—struggling at uni and battling to get your book finished. If you change your situation, then you won't feel depressed anymore. And for you, that means getting *Chrysalis* finished and doing well at uni. That's the key to you beating your depression.'

It's what I'd been thinking all along: *I've been depressed because I haven't been achieving my goals, so if I achieve my goals then I won't be depressed anymore.* To me, that line of thinking made sense. *So what's the need to see a psychologist?* I thought. *I don't need therapy to "change the way I think", and in any sense, I've got Sylvia to talk through my problems with. Like she said in her last message, she'll always be there for me, so seeing a psychologist would be redundant. It would only waste time that could better be spent working towards achieving my goals, so it would actually do* harm *rather than good. So it's out of the question. No way am I going to see a psychologist.*

This was the first time—and unfortunately not the last—where I put my faith in Dr Kramenin's hands and he fucked me over.

July, 2009

There were still days when I was horribly depressed, when I would've rather be anyone else than me, when I wanted to lock myself in my room and drink myself to death. But on the whole, I was feeling much better than I did when I got back from South America. The bad days were becoming fewer and farther between, and I was starting to return, ever so slowly, back into my usual confident, exuberant self. It was coming at the right time, too—Sylvia was an instructor at a holiday camp until September and barely had access to the internet, so she wouldn't have been able to support me if I crashed and burned again.

Without a doubt, the antidepressants were one reason why I'd been feeling a lot better. I'd definitely been more stable and level-headed since I'd been on them, instead of getting suicidal over the slightest thing all the time like I was before. But what'd also been great was having been able to settle into a routine where I got to spend the majority of the day doing what I loved: writing. As usual it filled me with enormous pleasure, and what's more, around that time I started discovering how cathartic writing could be, which enabled me to enjoy it on a whole new level. It was interesting—over the course of the year, I found myself putting so much of my soul into my novel. For example, when my protagonist was living in a shanty town and struggling to make ends meet, I made him turn to alcohol to escape. When he failed to reach the target amount of money that he wanted to make in a day, I had him falling into depression. At one point, I had him on the edge of a bridge about to jump. Hell, even the relationship between the protagonist and his lover started to mirror mine and Sylvia's, in the sense that it played a big role in helping him through his despair.

It was no accident that this happened—nearly all artists explore their struggles through their work. It helps us deal with it in a way. When I was writing about how my protagonist overcame his alcoholism, it reminded me that I needed to keep it together and not relapse. When I was writing about how he didn't jump off the bridge because he decided that he'd rather face his demons and beat them instead of running away, it reinforced the idea that I needed to stay strong and do the same. When I was writing about him achieving his dream at the end of the novel, it helped me remember that if I just kept working hard and never gave up, then I too could achieve mine. In this way, my protagonist became the man that I wanted to be. He helped give me strength, helped give me hope, helped me keep believing that my best days were ahead. He helped inspire me to keep on going.

By July, the next draft was almost finished. I planned to send it to Nick by the end of the month.

I really hope he says it's ready to be published this time, I remember thinking.

August, 2009

Dear Danny,

First off, I'd like to say that this draft is much, much better than your last one. You really brought the time period to life, and a lot of the silly schoolboy symbolism you used beforehand was eliminated. The ending was far less contrived. Good job.

However, I still feel you have a significant amount of work to do before you submit your novel for publication.

Just like last time, Nick then went on to detail the problems with the draft. Firstly, he said that although my writing style had improved immensely, that the novel still wasn't as well written as it needed to be. Secondly, the hardships that befell the protagonist occurred too close together, making large chunks of the novel too dark to be enjoyable. With regards to the main character falling in love with a black girl, Nick said that I still hadn't portrayed the "racial" issue anywhere near well enough. He also said that the poetry still wasn't up to scratch.

Part of me was encouraged: *Nick says it's much better than my last draft, so that's obviously a positive sign. It's good that I've been improving, and because I'll continue working hard and never give up, I have no doubt that one day, I'll have produced a novel that's worthy of being published.* I really did believe that. What I was worried about, however, was my dwindling amount of time. *What if I can't make all these changes before uni starts?* I stressed. *Then I won't get a High Distinction average. Then I'm going to be depressed. Then I'm going to want to kill myself again.*

I can't put myself through that again, I thought. *I just can't. So come hell or high water, I need to get this book finished by the end of the year.*

September, 2009

I started getting involved in quite a bit of volunteer work in the second half of the year. In August I did the 40 Hour Famine to raise money for World Vision, and in September I signed up to participate in Movember to fundraise for prostate cancer research and the mental health charity Beyond Blue. I guess I felt like I was doing my bit, but I really wanted to be doing more.

I kept thinking back to the poverty I saw in Peru: the skinny kids wearing World Vision clothes every day; the 10 year olds selling cigarettes on the streets at two o'clock in the morning on a school night; and the tiny homes made out of mud bricks. When I was there, I promised myself that I was going to make a difference once I got back to Sydney, so while I was raising money for Movember, I started looking into the feasibility of founding my own charity to help the people I worked with in Peru and others like them around the world.

'But is now really the best time for you to be starting up a charity?' Mum questioned. 'It's a nice idea, but right now, you're suffering from depression—you're hardly in the best state of mind yourself. Don't you think you should just focus on you for the time being and then worry about helping others once you're 100% healthy?'

I shook my head.

'I am going through a hard time right now, but eventually I'm going to work my way out of it. I'm going to beat my depression. I'm going to be OK. But those kids . . . they need people to help them. They're not in a position to be able to save themselves.'

I paused.

'I am in such a position to help them though, and I don't want to put off doing so any longer. I want to help them now.'

I paused again.

'Every day those kids are suffering—when you look at it like that, I've already waited long enough.'

October, 2009

I had my good days and my bad days, just like anyone else—but on my bad days I felt suicidal, and wanted nothing more than to put a gun to my head and blow my brains out. That was more or less the state of my depression in October, and I figured it to remain that way until I achieved my goals, because it was when I struggled to achieve them that I was sent spiralling into despair. With only one subject at uni at that point in time, my mood was basically pinned to my writing. If I felt like *Chrysalis* was on track to being well and truly finished by the start of the first semester of 2010, then I felt good. If I felt like it was still going to be at the draft stage, then I wanted to die. It was that simple, really.

November, 2009

Towards the end of the year, I found myself developing feelings for Sylvia. I knew we lived on opposite sides of the world, I knew we'd been friends for years and it was a dangerous line to cross, but the heart wants what the heart wants. I just kept thinking about how she'd always been there for me, about how she'd always helped me in my hours of need. No matter what I'd told her she'd always stuck by me, lifting me up again, giving me hope, inspiring me to keep on fighting. Just like Olivia is for Jimmy, Sylvia was the most compassionate, genuine, caring girl I'd ever met, and I found myself wanting her, despite all the warning signs.

She was coming back to Sydney for two weeks after Christmas. My plan was to wait until then and then tell her how I felt.

December, 2009

When I sent the next draft of *Chrysalis* to Nick, I felt really good about it. I was confident that it was ready and that it wouldn't leak into the upcoming semester. But all I could do was nervously wait and see.

In the meantime, I founded my charity—I partnered with a friend and we made it happen. We called it the Open Skies Foundation, and once it was fully set up, we planned on funding projects that created sustainable change in Third World Countries. Our first one was going to be to build greenhouses in the villages I visited while I was in Peru; this would allow vegetables and flowers to be grown year-round instead of only 3-4 months a year using open air fields, and thus provide the community members with a sustainable source of food and income. But unfortunately we were still a while off from being able to fundraise, as there were a lot of burdensome and time-consuming legal and administrative hoops to jump through before we obtained the requisite license to do so. *I really wish there didn't have to be such a delay*, I remember thinking. *I really wish we could start right now.* The urge to make a difference burned so strongly inside me, particularly whenever I saw an old photo of one of those kids wearing World Vision clothes in Peru. But as with everything else in my life, I knew that I had to be patient, and trust that everything would work out well in the end. Frank and I had a clear vision, and we were dedicated to growing Open Skies so that one day it would be operating in Third World Countries all over the world. That was our goal: to change hundreds of lives across the globe. It was not a commitment for the next month, or the next year, or even for the next decade, but rather a lifelong pledge to help those less fortunate than ourselves. Once again, it was those words that inspired me:

'Remember, Danny: to whom much is given, much is expected.'

January, 2010

We held each other in bed, gazing into one another's eyes. It was the end of a two week fling—she was heading back to the States the next day.

'What am I going to do without you?' I asked seriously.

She laughed.

'What are you talking about?'

I was thinking about how warm, how tender, how loving, how supportive she'd been through thick and thin. She was my rock, my saviour, and I couldn't bear to see her go.

'I'm going to miss you so much,' I said. 'Sydney won't be the same without you.'

'I'll miss you too. But we'll always have Facebook.'

It didn't seem like enough anymore. Our two weeks together had been amazing, and I'd fallen head over heels for her. *How can we go back to talking only once or twice a week over the net?* I thought.

'Maybe I could come and visit you sometime?' I asked.

I expected her to be excited at the prospect, but instead she looked shocked.

'Huh?' she gaped.

'Well, I've never been to mainland America before. You could show me around. It would be so nice to see you again.'

She looked away.

'Uh . . . well . . . I don't know. Let's not think about it right now, OK?'

I looked into her eyes and smiled, still not sure what I'd done to deserve someone as caring as her.

February, 2010

This is great! I thought. *I just got my review back from Nick, and he says* Chrysalis *is more or less finished! All I have to do is make a few changes, tinker with a few scenes here and there, tidy up the writing style in various places and I'll have a completed product! That's incredible! Particularly after everything I've been through! It's been such a long, slow, arduous process that's really tested my resolve, but I got there in the end and here I am, soon to be submitting my manuscript to agents and publishers. I can't wait!*

Uni's also starting in a couple of weeks. I'm taking all third-year economics subjects, including all the honours stream ones. I'm not quite sure exactly what line of work I want to pursue in the corporate world, but I know it's definitely not law. In fact, that's why I'm taking the honours stream subjects—once I've finished this year and gotten my Bachelor of Commerce, I'm almost certain that I'm going to quit my law degree and do an honours year in economics, followed by a Masters of Applied Finance at hopefully Oxford or Cambridge or one of the Ivy League schools in the States. Honours in economics and then an MAF will have me very well placed to get a job at one of the top management consulting firms in the world, which is the industry I'm leaning towards entering. It all starts with this year though, and I want to smash a High Distinction average and finish my bachelors on a high. And now that I've more or less finished my novel I'm primed and ready for it. Bring it on!

I feel as if I'm in a really good place right now. For the first time since uni started, I'm really pleased with the direction my corporate career, my writing and my charity work is heading in, and that's something to really feel good about. Now that my goals are on track to being achieved, I feel like I'm back to my old self again. Once again I'm full of hope and confidence, brimming with energy, coursing with desire. And my depression? That's long gone. Done, finished, kaput. Goodbye, you bitch. I've beaten you. You tried to break me but you couldn't.

With the benefit of hindsight, it is easy to see that ignorance is bliss.

PART III

OR

'THANK-YOU, DR

GREGOR'

OR

'FUCK YOU, DR

KRAMENIN'

March, 2010

On the first day of my Advanced Microeconomics Honours class, the professor ran us through the course outline and the assessment regime before delving straight into game theory in extensive form. Within a few minutes I was horribly lost. I had no idea what was going on. I tried my best to catch up while the lecture continued:

'It is imperative to note the critical distinction between actions and strategies. Suppose player "I" in an extensive form game has "L" information sets: "I.1", "I.2" . . . "I.L" etcetera, and that she has a choice of M_K actions at her "K-th" information set. Then, player "I" has "M_1" x "M_2" x . . . x "M_K" strategies. If an agent has only one information set, strategies and actions are synonymous for that player. In particular, for a simultaneous-move game, the notions of strategies and actions coincide for each player.'

I was so confused. *What the fuck is he talking about?* My notes were a mess—he was speaking far too quickly for me to get everything down. I scanned the room in panic, hoping to see everyone just as lost as I was, but they were all listening intently and calmly taking notes. Some students were even asking perceptive questions that pleased the lecturer. But I still had no idea what was going on. I started berating myself.

What the fuck is wrong with me? How the fuck is it that everyone understands what's going on except for me? Everyone here must be smarter than me. Hell, of course they're smarter than me. I'm dumb. I'm an idiot. I'm a fuckwit. I'm a complete and utter failure.

And the more I abused myself the less I could concentrate, and the less I could concentrate the more I fell behind. In two hours I hardly absorbed anything, and all my old demons—anxious dread, self-loathing and a lust for death—stormed back into my life and butchered my psyche.

I left class feeling suicidal. Despair throttled me, as did that torturous uncertainty of not knowing whether or not I'd ever be able to douse depression's roaring fires that once again were burning me alive.

For fuck's sake! I thought I was cured! I felt cured. But I'm not. I'm as depressed as ever.

I fought back tears.

Will I ever get better? I fretted. *Is this just the way I am? Am I forever destined to a life of excruciating misery?*

I went home and tried to work through the lecture material but I was too depressed to function. I took a break and tried again, but it was the same story all night long. Eventually I gave up and tried to get some sleep, although I should've known there was no chance of me being able to just shut my eyes and drift away. I was far too disturbed. I was far too terrified. I was in full-blown panic mode.

I just couldn't believe it.

How the fuck can it be back?

How the fuck can my depression possibly be back?

~~~

Sylvia, where've you been? I'm going fucking mad here. My depression's back and I don't know what to do. What am I supposed to do? My doctor's put me on a stronger antidepressant but it's not making any difference. Nothing is. Fuck. Just please say something to help me. I'm going to pieces and I really need your support.

Love,

Danny.

~~~

I was more depressed than ever. It started on my first day back at uni when I left class feeling like a failure, and was multiplied by the horrifying reality that I'd never in fact conquered my depression and maybe never would. Feeling that depressed made it difficult to study, so I fell behind at uni, which made me even more depressed, which made it even more difficult to study, which made me even more depressed . . . and so the cycle went. The pain lasted for days at a time. To use Jimmy's analogy in *I Will Not Kill Myself, Olivia,* I felt like a starving journeyman lost deep in a forest, blindly wandering in the hope of making it out alive. The journeyman has no food. He goes for three or four days, sometimes even a week, without eating. Eventually he'll catch something, wolf it down, but it's only a quick fix. Not long after he'll be famished again. Replace hunger with depression and that was me. Food was my equivalent to all forms of escape: T.V., reading and masturbation. They were temporary as fuck. Depression always prevailed.

I would think of suicide as much as the starving journeyman would think of food. We had the same goal, too: get through the day. Live til tomorrow. Sometimes that seemed too overwhelming, so I'd use the trick my addictions psychologist taught me and break it down into smaller sub-goals: *just survive the next twelve hours. The next ten hours. Hold off killing yourself until then.* It was so hard but I knew that I had to keep on fighting, I knew I couldn't lose faith that one day I'd get better. Every day I prayed to the Lord: *God . . . I am suffering . . . I am drained . . . please give me strength . . . please give me the fortitude to beat this illness.* My life was such a disaster but I had not abandoned hope. That's the one thing I had going for me. To steal another line from *I Will Not Kill Myself, Olivia,* hope and depression are bitter rivals until one inevitably defeats the other. As long as I had hope I was in with a shot.

~~~

Sylvia, what's going on? I've tried texting you but you won't reply to my messages. Everything's so fucked up. I don't know how to beat this illness and I'm just getting worse and worse and worse. I'm so lost. So confused. Help me. Please.

~~~

I kept floundering, kept sinking. One night in particular stands out in my mind. It was three in the morning. I lay on a couch paralysed with anguish. I was in so much mental agony that it was affecting me physically. I felt so heavy, so lethargic. I could hardly move. Hardly speak. Mum was beside me, clutching my hand. Tears were rolling down her cheeks.

'D-Danny . . .' she sobbed. 'Danny pr-promise . . . promise me you'll never . . . end your life . . .'

She clenched my hand even tighter.

'Do you promise?'

I managed to move my head, nod ever so slightly.

'Because if you do . . .' she cried, 'you might as well take me with you.'

I knew I'd never do it. *No matter how much I want to I can't commit suicide,* I thought. *Suicide's quitting. Suicide's selfish. I am not a quitter, and I'm not going to leave my family without a brother and a son.*

'Don't worry,' I murmured. 'I won't.'

~~~

Sylvia, what's with you lately? You never reply to texts, take ages to reply to Facebook messages, and don't want to talk on the phone. Something about you seems so . . . distant. Seems so foreign. It's like I . . . don't even know you anymore. Seriously, Sylvia . . . what's going on?

~~~

Look, Danny—maybe I have been distancing myself from you lately, but I have my reasons. You're depending on me more and more and . . . I care about you, OK, and I want to be there for you—but you've got to understand that it's putting a hell of a lot of pressure on me.

I'm only human, Danny, and I'm not a qualified psychologist either. I'm your friend, OK? I've been supporting you as your friend and I want to keep doing so, but you have got to realise that it can be very hard for me, particularly when all you seem to feel is depressed these days. You're not even seeing a psychologist, so you're depending solely on me. Not to mention that your feelings for me are growing and growing and you're contacting me at rapidly increasing rates and . . . look, it's all just a lot of pressure, OK? It's scary. It's too much for me right now and I don't know how to deal with it.

Just like Olivia eventually does, Sylvia was beginning to reach the end of her tether.

~~~

We talked back and forth for the next few days, but everything basically came to a boil. Sylvia was feeling uncomfortable about the extent to which I was coming to her with my problems and about how attached I was getting to her, and once she aired those sentiments, I felt too self-conscious and uncomfortable to talk to her at all. So that was pretty much the end of it.

The timing couldn't have been worse. As if I wasn't depressed enough already, I'd now messed things up with Sylvia, a very important person in my life and my main support system. It was depression on top of depression. A whole new low.

In a moment of reflection, I found myself thinking back over every attempt I'd made in the last two years to try and beat my illness: trying to drink my way out of it; working myself to exhaustion at uni and on my novel; snorting coke in South America; working my ass off again on my novel and at uni; depending on Sylvia for help and support. *And where has it gotten me?* I thought. *I'm an alcoholic, suicidal on a daily basis, and I just lost Sylvia because I smothered her too much.*

There was no escaping the cold hard reality:

Nothing I have tried to beat my depression has worked. Every one of my attempts has failed.

I released an exhausted sigh before reality landed me another kick in the balls:

I don't know how to fix my depression.

Admit it: I've got no idea how to fix my depression.

'Danny, will you *please* see a psychologist,' my mother begged.

I knew Dr Kramenin said I didn't need to see one, but I felt like I was out of options. I was the most depressed I'd ever been, and I didn't know where else to turn.

'OK, Mum,' I said. 'I'll see a psychologist.'

April, 2010

It took all of my energy to heave myself out of bed and make it to my first appointment. I arrived at Dr Gregor's office feeling dreadful, and sat slouched in the waiting room with my head lulled lethargically back against the wall until he called me in. He was a tall, middle-aged man with brown hair, an unassuming posture and soft, gentle features. His handshake was prolonged, full of the warm familiarity of a mate, and his smile was broad and friendly, inducing me to reciprocate even though I felt like shit. When he introduced himself he spoke in a calm, soothing voice and looked me earnestly in the eye. My immediate impression of him was that he was an amiable, down to earth bloke who wouldn't judge me no matter what I told him.

He led me from the waiting room into his office, where we sat down in comfortable arm chairs that faced each other. Then without further ado, I described to him everything I'd been through. I'd always thought it would be difficult—opening up my soul and sharing my darkest, innermost thoughts to a stranger—but Dr Gregor was warm and non-judgmental, and even if he wasn't, I felt far too depressed to give a shit what he thought of me anyway.

'And the worst part is,' I finally summed up, 'that I don't know what more I can do to beat my depression. I've worked so hard on my book and at uni but it's never enough. I always fall back into it. I keep thinking I've beaten it but it always comes back. I've tried everything to beat it but it always comes back.

Dr Gregor frowned gently.

'I don't think that's true, Danny,' he said.

'You don't think what's true?'

'That you've tried everything you can to beat your depression.'

'But I have,' I insisted. 'For two years I busted my ass but no combination of writing and studying worked to achieve my goals. Then I took a year off purely to write—I delayed my corporate career an entire year!—and that didn't work either. And now I'm back at uni and trying my best but it's still not enough. Nothing's changed. I've worked as hard as I can but I'm still so depressed.'

'That's not what I mean,' he said calmly.

'What do you mean, then?'

'In all the time you've been depressed—two years, now—have you ever once seen a psychologist?'

'Yes.'

'For depression?'

'No, for alcoholism.'

'What about for depression?'

'No.'

'Never?'

I shook my head.

'This is my first ever session.'

'Why didn't you see a psychologist earlier?' he asked.

'Because I didn't think I needed to. I thought that all I needed to do to beat my depression was to get a High Distinction average and get my novel published. I thought that after I achieved my goals I'd be happy again. That's what my GP's been telling me—fix your situation and you'll stop feeling depressed.'

Dr Gregor's eyebrows jumped.

'Your GP told you that?'

'That's what he always tells me.'

Dr Gregor shook his head.

'I don't think that's very good advice,' he said.

I was surprised.

'How do you mean?'

He sighed.

'Let me put it this way: what's going to happen if you don't achieve your goals? Are you going to be depressed forever?'

I flinched. It was such a brazen, confronting question.

'I . . . I mean . . . I think I will achieve them. But if I don't . . . if I don't I'll . . .'

'Even if you do achieve them this time round, what about your goals after that? What if you struggle to achieve those, just like you've struggled with uni and your novel? Does that mean you'll go through another huge bout of depression? And what about your goals after that, and the ones after that? Are you going to get depressed every time they don't go 100% according to plan?'

I was speechless. My whole world was crashing down around me. I was so sure that all I needed to do to beat my depression forever was to get a High Distinction average and get my novel published. That's what Dr Kramenin had always told me, and to me, it had always made sense. But the questions Dr Gregor was asking me . . . I'd never thought of them before. And now that I was, my life seemed destined to be bereft of happiness. It seemed that my depression would keep coming back, again and again and again, until the day I died Consternation engulfed me. I was so scared that I literally wanted to puke.

'Yes,' I managed to croak.

Dr Gregor nodded.

'This is why the advice Dr Kramenin gave you wasn't very good. All he told you to do to fix your depression was to change your situation, and as you can see, in your case at least, this would have set you up for a lifetime of relapses. Now, sometimes overcoming depression *is* as simple as changing your situation—but often the reason people suffer from depression is not actually because of their situation itself, but rather because of the way they *think about* their situation. And this is what I think your problem is—one of perception, as opposed to one of circumstance. You feel suicidal every time you struggle or "fail", as you put it, to achieve your goals—and it doesn't have to be this way. My role as your psychologist will be to help you get to the bottom of why "failing" to achieve your goals depresses you so much, and then help you to perceive this "failure" in a way that doesn't make you feel depressed.'

At the time, it seemed unimaginable. But I tried to be hopeful.

'Do you really think I can get to that place?' I asked.

He nodded.

'If you commit yourself to therapy, then I'm confident you can.'

Our session eventually finished. I agreed to see Dr Gregor again at the end of the week, and we shook hands and parted. What he'd said sounded promising, but I just couldn't for the life of me ever envision a world where not getting a High Distinction average or my novel published didn't plunge me into a life-threatening bout of depression. Hell, in the state I was in then, anything but depression seemed impossible to fathom.

~~~

The new medication Dr Kramenin prescribed was giving me splitting headaches, so he placed me on a different one yet again—this time a relatively new drug that was part of the serotonin-norepinephrine reuptake inhibitor class of antidepressants. Mum was hysterical over it.

'Danny, you should *not* be taking that medication! In Beyond Blue's *Clinical Practise Guidelines for Depression in Adolescents and Young Adults*, it specifically states that for the type of drug you've been placed on, further research is required before any conclusions can be drawn about its effectiveness and harms. For this reason, its use is *not* recommended for adolescents or young adults under the age of 24.'

'But Dr Kramenin prescribed it, so it must be OK.'

'That does *not* mean it's OK! All that proves is that he hasn't read the guidelines!'

'He's the GP, Mum! I'm not going to go against what he says!'

'I don't care if he's the GP! You need to tell him to change medications again! You can't keep taking this one! You're only twenty-*one*!'

We argued about it for hours, and eventually I was able to get Mum off my back. She was still distraught about the antidepressant I was taking, but the matter of my medication was just one too many things for me to deal with at that point.

I'm just trying to get through the days without necking myself, I remember thinking. *What medication I'm on is up to Dr Kramenin. It's his job to make sure I'm taking the right one.*

~~~

The days dragged along. This was the worst I'd ever felt. Period. There was no relief from the ceaseless dread. I could barely function. Paying attention in class was almost impossible. Studying was too overwhelming. I'd fallen absurdly behind. I hadn't touched my book in days. I'd quit my job at the law firm, too—needed all my free time to try and catch up on uni. But there was never enough time. I was constantly exhausted. Drained of life. Depression sucked at my soul. My spirit withered. My goal for the day got broken down even further: *just survive the next six hours. The next four hours. Hold off killing yourself until then.*

I'd previously thought I'd get better. I'd always thought it true that hope and depression were bitter rivals until one inevitably defeated the other, and I'd always thought that hope would win out in the end. But for the first time in my life, I was void of hope. I honestly believed that being depressed was just the way I was, and that being depressed was just the way I'd be, for the rest of my life. And because I was so convinced that I'd never get better, there seemed no point in fighting my illness. Instead of willing myself to "hang in there" because I believed that my suffering was temporary and that everything would be better one day, I comforted myself with the knowledge that human beings are not immortal. That I would die, one day. One special, glorious day. Then I could spend the rest of eternity mouldering in a grave, free from pain. You might be wondering why I didn't just kill myself if I wholeheartedly believed that my future consisted of nothing more than excruciating misery. Well, first of all, I still was not a quitter. But more importantly, I didn't want to hurt the people that loved me.

It's not fair to commit suicide and ruin their lives, I thought. *So I have to hold on. No matter how much it hurts me I have to hold on.*

Hence why I drew comfort from the thought that one day I'd die and finally be free.

When you're that depressed, that insanely and utterly depressed that you genuinely believe you'll suffer that acutely for the rest of your days, life seems to lack all purpose. *After all,* I remember thinking, *what's the point in working, fighting, striving for a better life if I'm sentenced to one of chronic anguish and despair? There is no better life. There is no life outside of pain. So what's the point in doing anything but waiting until death finally arrives on my doorstep and whisks me away to the Promised Land?* I was still studying, and I still planned on finishing my novel and trying to get it published, but it was more out of force of habit than anything else. My passion had been drained. My zest for life asphyxiated. I was like a ghost, just drifting through the ghastly days.

'Shit! What's wrong, mate?' an old friend once said when I ran into him at uni. 'Perk up, brother!'

I was shocked. One of the most well-known attributes of depression is that it is entirely possible—and very common—to suffer horrifically without anybody knowing. But somehow without realising it, I'd crossed the line from a place where I was able to put on a front and fool people into thinking I wasn't depressed to a place where I was so sick that it was obvious to people I hadn't even seen for a year. When I got home I looked in the bathroom mirror, and realised that I was staring back at a man whose eyes were exhausted slits, whose whole face shrieked of agonising misery. I was staring back at a man whose spirit had been broken, whose soul had been destroyed. I was staring back at a man who, for all intents and purposes, was already dead.

Three days later

I'd always taken a lot of pride in being a fighter, which in my books, meant having a tremendous work ethic, relentless determination, and most importantly, a never-say-die attitude. And because I was a fighter, I'd always believed I could handle anything life threw at me, and that even though I may struggle and fall, I'd get up every time and succeed in the end. That'd been my MO, and that's what I hung my confidence on.

But drifting through life a spiritless, broken shell of a man?

Giving up on happiness and resigning to a life of misery?

Letting depression destroy the next 60 years of my life?

That's not fighting, I finally realised. That's quitting. And that's not me. I'm not going to let depression break me. Not now, not ever. I don't know when, I don't know how, but somehow I'm going to beat this illness and live a happy, healthy, fulfilling life.

May, 2010

It took five intense weeks to understand the issue forming the crux of my depression—the "underlying issue", as Dr Gregor chose to call it. Over that time we were able to dig deep into my psyche, and after analysing my behaviour and the way I thought, Dr Gregor concluded that the primary culprit of my depression was a very unhealthy level of perfectionism.

'You relentlessly seek excellence, Danny, and you always set extremely challenging goals and then throw yourself into achieving them. Being perfectionistically goal-driven like this is fine in and of itself, but the problem with you is that you measure your self-worth entirely in terms of whether or not you achieve these goals. If you don't achieve a goal that you set out to achieve—like getting a High Distinction average or getting your novel published by a particular point in time—you hate yourself. You feel worthless and inadequate. You feel like a failure. And you feel this pain so intensely that you'd rather be dead.

'You're human, Danny, and humans, by our very composition, are not perfect. Humans make mistakes. Humans don't always achieve their goals. You need to accept this, and not be so hard on yourself. You need to accept this, and be able to love yourself regardless. You need to be able to love yourself regardless of how you go in your uni exams and no matter what happens with your novel. Even if you fail every exam for the rest of your degree and your novel never gets published, you should still be able to love yourself. You should be able to find elements of yourself that you love that will be there no matter what. That will let you love yourself no matter what.'

He paused for a moment.

'If you can do this, then I think you'll go a long way towards conquering your depression.'

~~~

Over the next several days, I managed to find things about myself that I liked. The fact that it took me an entire week to do so may seem downright absurd to you—maybe you can list a dozen things you like about yourself right off the top of your head. But me? I sure as hell couldn't do it. It wasn't something I'd ever considered before. All that mattered to me was whether or not I was achieving my goals. If I was, or was on track to, then I loved myself. If I hadn't, or was not on track to, then I hated myself. The concept of loving myself regardless of whether or not I succeeded was completely foreign to me.

But after a long time pondering, I finally had a list written:

- *I like it that I'm a kind person—someone who always treats other people with respect.*

- *I like it that I'm an honest person who acts with integrity.*

- *I like it that I'm compassionate and that I do volunteer work to try and help other people less fortunate than myself.*

- *I like it that I have the determination and the work ethic to pursue my dreams through to completion.*

- *I like the fact that I'm a positive person. I like the fact that even after everything I've been though, I still feel tremendously blessed, still feel immensely fortunate to have everything the Lord has bestowed upon me. I like the fact that instead of thinking of myself as unlucky for having suffered such a severe depression, I think of myself as lucky for having all the support I'm getting to help me beat it.*

- *I like it that I'm religious—that I have God in my life to guide me and to keep me safe. I like it that I trust Him so deeply that I'm faithful no matter what.*

- *I like it that I'm a fighter. I like it that I can handle everything life throws at me, and that even though I may struggle and fall, I have the strength to get up every time and beat it in the end.*

And when I focused on those things, I could actually see that there really was a lot to love about me.

I actually am a good person, I thought. *And this really is true, regardless of what my marks are at uni or whether or not my novel ever gets published. These are the reasons why I can love myself, and whether I succeed or fail has nothing to do with it.*

~~~

For the next few days it was all I could think about—this idea of thinking of myself as an inherently good person and loving myself regardless of whether I succeeded or failed. And its strength, its conviction, only grew with time. For the first time in a very long time I was really able to see the good in me, and now that I could, I didn't feel worthless anymore. I didn't hate myself. I didn't feel inadequate. Instead, I felt confident, and proud of myself. And I didn't feel depressed at all.

~~~

I shared my psychological epiphany with Dr Gregor the next time I saw him.

'This is excellent, Danny,' he said. 'Measuring your self-worth entirely in terms of productivity and accomplishment is not healthy—but this—what you've just told me—*is*. And combined with you taking your new medication which now seems to be working, I think it's the key to you overcoming your depression.'

Hearing that made me feel so empowered, so unburdened. But it also made me feel a pang of unease.

'But Dr Gregor . . . I like being a perfectionist. I like setting challenging goals for myself and then working hard to achieve them. Are you saying that it's not healthy to do that?'

He shook his head.

'Of course not, Danny. It's perfectly healthy to have goals and to pursue them passionately. It's good, even, and you should continue to do it. But it's critical that you love yourself, regardless of whether or not you achieve those goals.'

He paused.

'There are many good aspects of perfectionism, Danny. Like we've said, it obviously pushes one to strive for excellence and to reach their true potential. And in your case, I suspect it was the underlying reason why you never killed yourself. To you, suicide would've been quitting––the ultimate failure. And there is nothing, *nothing* a perfectionist hates more than failing.'

He paused again.

'It's a double-edged sword, perfectionism. The challenge for you, Danny, is going to be to retain the positives of it while banishing the negatives. And if you can remember and apply what we've talked about today, then I think you'll be able to do it. I *know* you'll be able to do it.'

~~~

Two weeks later, I was waiting at my computer to get the results of my Mathematical Economics mid-semester exam mark back. Due to my work with Dr Gregor I'd been feeling much better over the last few weeks, and with a few all-nighters and help from my friends, I was able to catch up on most of the uni work I'd missed out on. I'd done well in my mid-semester exams so far, getting 80% for Monetary Economics, 88% for Advanced Microeconomics Honours, and 90% for Regression

Modelling. I'd run out of time to properly catch up on Math Econ, so I knew I wouldn't go as well in that—but I was hopeful I could scrape together a 75 and, due to the other exams being worth more, have my marks balance out to a High Distinction average.

Five PM came. I logged in and went to the "Exam Results" section.

Nine out of 20.

Nine.

Forty-five per cent.

A fail.

I couldn't believe it. I'd never failed an exam at uni before. Never even come close. I was absolutely gutted. *Fucking hell,* I thought. *A mark like this is really going to drag my average down. It's really going to make it difficult to get a High Distinction average this semester. This is bad. This is fucked. Fuck fuck fuck fuck fuck.*

I stewed in disappointment for the next half an hour before deciding to get laced up and head to the gym. I popped into the bathroom before I went, and then it hit me while I was taking a piss.

Wow! I actually exclaimed out loud. *I just got a shocking exam mark and I didn't go to pieces! I didn't abuse myself! I don't feel inadequate. I don't feel suicidal. I only feel disappointed. Not depressed—just disappointed!*

I could hardly believe it. Before I saw Dr Gregor, an exam mark like that would've destroyed me. It would've made me feel horribly inadequate and plunged me into an almost suicidal depression. But now, all I felt was disappointment—a perfectly healthy emotion. *I've had a setback, yes,* I thought, *but that doesn't mean I'm worthless. It doesn't mean I'm a failure. I'll learn where I went wrong, I'll do better next time, and I'll go on to live a happy, fulfilling life. That's all there is to it.*

Wow, I thought to myself. *I never thought I'd say this on a day I failed an exam, but I actually feel great right now. I think I've finally conquered my demons. God sent me a huge test, and I passed with flying colours! Regardless of how I went in my exam today, I truly have succeeded.*

I never thought I'd say that, either.

~~~

I told Dr Gregor what happened with my exam mark at our appointment a few days later.

'That's great, Danny!' he beamed. 'That's really, really great.'

I was beaming too. The high hadn't worn off yet.

'I feel really good,' I said. 'I think I've actually conquered my depression. Once and for all, this time.'

Dr Gregor nodded.

'You've done exceptionally well in these last couple of months, Danny. You came to me an emotional wreck, and you've transformed yourself into a brand new man. You ought to be congratulated. I know it hasn't been easy but you've done a great job.'

I smiled at him gratefully.

'Thank-you so much for all your help, Dr Gregor. Like you said I was such a mess when I first came to see you, but now I really do feel well again.'

I paused for a moment, looking him earnestly, emotionally in the eye.

'You've saved my life,' I said.

He smiled at me and we shared a warm moment together.

July, 2010

Halfway through the year, I finally finished *Chrysalis*. It took me the rest of the semester plus all of the holiday break, but I eventually managed to work in all of Nick's comments and do enough final read-throughs for me to be entirely happy with it and feel that at last it was ready to submit to literary agents. The way it usually worked was that you had to submit a one page "query letter" describing your novel; based on that, the agent might ask to read your manuscript, and if they liked it, they might offer to represent you. Once you've been signed, your agent would then present your work to publishing houses to try and get you a deal. It would be a long process, and it all began with the query letter, so I started reading everything I could find on the internet about how best to write them, after which I planned to write, rewrite and profusely edit my own. It was kind of like writing a second novel in the sense that it had to be as close to perfect as possible before you submitted it to an agent. You could write a great book but if the query letter wasn't up to par then you wouldn't get anywhere, so it was well worth taking the time to get it right.

~~~

Uni was due to start at the end of July, and once again I was aiming to get that so far elusive High Distinction average. I got almost 80% in the first semester, which, while disappointing, Dr Gregor had taught me to view as actually pretty good, considering the circumstances. That was something we were constantly working on—trying to get me to not be so hard on myself, to offer myself compassion, to learn to think of things in shades of grey rather than so black and white. No more *80% < 85% = fail*. Rather, *it's good, considering that for half the semester I was* *really sick, and now that I'm well again I'll work hard to achieve my goal this time.* That sort of stuff.

I felt good at the time. I could feel myself getting healthier and healthier, due to all the therapy I'd been continuing to do, and I was excited to embark upon my publication journey and jump right back into uni. I felt it was time to start a new chapter in my life, one where I was depression-free and ready to achieve my goals.

August, 2010

Mum was still stressing out about the medication I was on.

'You shouldn't be taking this antidepressant, Danny! You're too young! Like I keep trying to tell you, it's not recommended for young adults under the age of 24!'

'Mum I'm sick of talking about this! I'm doing well now—I don't want to change medications. And Dr Kramenin doesn't want me to, either.'

'Dr Kramenin hasn't read the research! He's got no idea what he's doing! Don't you get it? Not enough research has been done on this drug to know its effects on young adults under 24! You're like a guinea pig! Who knows what's going to happen down the line?'

'Dr Kramenin said it's fine.'

'Dr Kramenin doesn't know what he's doing!'

'Mum can you just drop it?'

'But Danny—'

'I said drop it, Mum! I told you—I'm sick of talking about this!'

~~~

Throughout the year, my co-founder and I had been working hard to get Open Skies off the ground. We were making progress, but unfortunately everything was moving at a snail's pace. We were still waiting on receiving the government's approval for our License to Fundraise, and until then were forced to play the waiting game with great frustration. In the meantime though, I'd started doing volunteer work at 180 Degrees Consulting, which is a non-profit organisation that does pro-bono work for other NGOs. The first project I was assigned to do was to work closely with a charity that combatted violence against women. Broadly speaking, my team's role was to advise them how to achieve their objectives more efficiently, so we started breaking down the organisation into its various components and analysing where improvements could be made. Just like the previous charity work I'd done, it was a very eye-opening experience—as the project progressed, I gained a much deeper appreciation of the hardship that battered women endure, and also of some of the reasons why many victims can't just simply "pack their bags and leave"—often they have nowhere to go, are financially dependent on their abuser, think their abuser will kill them if they do, or can't bear to leave their children behind. In the same way witnessing Peru's confronting poverty did, learning about the suffering of these poor women shed even more light on just how lucky I really was, and further strengthened my belief that as someone who'd been tremendously blessed, it was my obligation to help those less fortunate than myself. Open Skies was my baby, my pet project, and as soon as we got our License to Fundraise I hoped to do incredible things with it—but in the meantime, I still wanted to do whatever I could to help others in need.

September, 2010

Things were still a mess with Sylvia. We tried to work through it but couldn't make any headway, and by September we weren't speaking at all. It'd been bothering me, so I started talking to Dr Gregor about it.

'I think the problem you guys had is that you had a very uneven relationship—and what I mean by that is that Sylvia was more your de facto therapist than your friend. You came to her with all your problems and she helped you through them, and the more this happened, the more you came to depend on her, the more emotionally attached you became to her, the higher a pedestal you placed her on and the more you thought of her as some sort of angel of healing, and the more, I suspect, she thought of you as something along the lines of a mentally ill patient in need of help. It got to the stage where you became needy and started asking too much of her, and that made her feel pressured and scared and she started putting up barriers, and when that started happening, it bothered you to such an extent that you felt too uncomfortable to ever open up to her again. And the end result is that you're no longer talking to each other.'

I was confused—not about Dr Gregor's analysis of mine and Sylvia's relationship specifically, but about the general conclusion that it seemed to be implying.

'But then . . . but then are you saying that it's not healthy to turn to a friend or a partner or whoever for support? Are you saying that it's healthier to just keep to yourself?'

He shook his head.

'Of course not, Danny. You never want to keep things bottled up inside you. It's good to talk to your friends, your partner and your family and to have their support, but when you have a mental illness, it's never good to rely on someone to such an extent that they become a *substitute* for a psychologist—which is exactly what was happening with you and Sylvia. It's not good for the relationship, as you've seen, and it's also detrimental to you on a broader level. When you have a mental illness and you rely on someone as a substitute for a psychologist, then you're not getting the help you need. Love and support from the people closest to you is invaluable, but it can't take the place of professional help. It needs to be in addition to it, not as a replacement for it. Think about it, Danny: if you had a physical illness or injury—a broken leg, diabetes or cancer for example—you'd never refuse professional help and rely solely on the support of your loved ones to get through it. And it's exactly the same with a mental illness— nothing should take the place of professional help.'

I nodded. It made sense, and I wished it was something I'd known earlier. It reminded me of that old adage "experience is the comb life gives you once you're already bald".

We kept talking.

'So do you think I'll ever be able to be friends with Sylvia again?' I asked.

Dr Gregor nodded.

'If you're both able to put the past behind you and start fresh, then I think you'll be fine. But don't rush it. Give it time. You're doing well now, Danny—the best advice I can give you is to just keep doing what you're doing. Keep focusing on getting better, keep honing your coping mechanisms so you don't have any relapses. Then you can see how things stand with Sylvia when the right time comes.'

To bring this sub-story to a close, it was a couple of years before we reconciled, but in 2013 Sylvia and I were able to start fresh and are now friends again. Just like Dr Gregor said, all we needed was time.

October, 2010

So after a lot of thinking, I finally settled on what I wanted to do in the corporate world: become a management consultant. According to my classmates and all the recruiters from the big firms who were always visiting the campus, you basically got paid a ton of money to travel all over the world and consult on a multitude of fascinating projects for a diverse range of organisations. It sounded great, particularly the part about getting paid a heap of money. *I could live the life I've always envisioned!* I thought excitedly. *I could own a big house on the harbour, have a couple of sports cars parked in the garage, and take my family on overseas holidays every year! How cool would that be?*

There was no one path to take to become a management consultant, but I planned on doing Economics Honours in 2011 followed by a Masters of Applied Finance at Oxford or Cambridge or one of the Ivy League schools in America. By then I would've had more than enough education under my belt to get a job at one of the top tier firms.

I decided not to finish my law degree. I found it dry and unenjoyable and it wasn't where my strengths lay. So I applied for honours and planned on quitting law as soon as I'd been officially accepted. But until then I had to focus on my bachelors. My exams were only a couple of weeks away, and I wanted to smash them and end my degree on a high.

November, 2010

How the fuck can this still be happening? After all I've been through . . . after all I've done to get better . . . how, for fuck's sake, how?

I was suicidal again.

For the first five days of November I was horribly depressed, and what was most bewildering was that I didn't know why. Unlike before, my depression didn't seem in the slightest bit related to my perfectionism. Whenever I'd been depressed in the past, it was because I thought I'd failed at something. I could always point to a "cause"— like a bad book review or an exam mark below 85%. But this time there was no such cause. I'd just wake up and want to die—that's it. And for that reason, I couldn't use any of the techniques Dr Gregor had taught me to work through my despair. Being reminded of all the reasons why I ought to love myself wasn't working this time.

I was so shocked. So mind-numbingly terrified. *For fuck's sake!* I stressed. *How could I feel so well again, feel so certain that I'd overcome my depression, only to have the urge to kill myself again? It's been three years now! I'm working with my psychologist, I'm taking my medication—what more can I possibly do?* Back came all the petrifying questions, the ones that would nosedive me even deeper into depression and chill me to the bone:

Will I ever beat this illness?

Is this just the way I am?

Am I destined to live a life that's forever riddled with suffering and despair?

Who knows? Who the fuck knows?

I wish I could kill myself, I remember thinking. *I wish I didn't have any family so that I could just blow my brains out and nobody would care.*

~~~

Then all of a sudden, life was sublimely rapturous.

The days are so beautiful! I remember thinking. *I'm so lucky to be alive! God, thank-you for the gift of life! For giving me the senses to be able to see, smell, hear, taste and touch this beautiful planet that you've graced us with! Thank-you for blessing me with everything anyone could possibly want! And please help everybody who's less fortunate than me . . . please help everybody who didn't wake up this morning feeling that today is a glorious gift from above!*

Wow! The world is just perfect! It's such a splendiferous oasis! Such a magnificent confluence of beauty! Like Victoria Park next to uni! I love just strolling around and marvelling at the gorgeous green grass, smiling at the ducks in the pond, picking flowers off the jacaranda trees and twirling them hypnotically between my fingers, which is seriously like, the most beautiful thing in the world. And how about technology these days! I mean talk about incredible! The fact that we can speak to people on the other side of the planet is absolutely amazing! I was chatting to an old flame the other day and I was just thinking, "how are we not together?" Like seriously, we would be so good for each other! It's like that letter I sent her last year with the flowers, when I was talking about picking them all and laying them at her proverbial feet, and it just made so much sense, and it still makes so much sense, because I'll treat her so well, and she gets me, like we really click! I don't know what my brother's talking about, saying that it doesn't make any sense. He doesn't make any sense! He doesn't understand how beautiful the world is! He doesn't understand how deliriously happy I am! Like, wow! This is the best I've ever felt in my entire life! I feel so invincible! So strong! So powerful! So indestructible! When I look up into the sky and sense the Lord's presence, it's like we're the same. I feel like God! I feel like God! I am so insurmountable that I feel like God!

~~~

And then I was depressed again.

I was depressed two days before my first final year exam.

I was depressed two days after the most blissfully happy week of my life.

And I still had no idea how.

What the fuck is going on? I remember thinking. *What the fuck is wrong with me?*

I was back in wanting-to-die mode, more so than ever before. I tried to escape through life's momentary pleasures: masturbating; over-eating; sleeping, if I could manage to get it. But it never lasted beyond the moment. Depression always prevailed.

I wish I didn't have any family, I kept thinking. *Then I could just end it.*

At the time, I remember feeling that love was a terrible burden.

~~~

A week later, I was back to being high as a kite. I felt so energetic, so vivacious, so almighty again. Dr Gregor said I was exhibiting classic symptoms of bipolar disorder—a condition where, when untreated, the sufferer oscillates between the nodes of extreme depression and extreme mania. I seemed to fit the description, but psychologists provide therapy as opposed to diagnose mental illnesses, so Dr Gregor advised me to see a psychiatrist. I really hoped someone could figure out what was wrong with me. I felt so wildly unstable, so horrifically disturbed. And the "mania", if that's in fact what my highs were, was really starting to freak the shit out of me. I liked it at first, I think because I was so relieved not to be depressed anymore. But after a while it was just plain fucking scary.

Feeling that I'm a superhero?

That I'm the greatest human being on earth?

That I'm as powerful as God?

Like what the fuck! That's so ridiculous! I mean seriously, what the fuck is wrong with me? I'm crazy! I'm actually crazy!

And the worst part was that I was actually aware of it. I *knew* that I'd lost my mind. I *knew* that I'd gone completely mad.

It was the most confronting, horrifying experience I'd ever had in my life. I'd rather have been suicidal any day.

~~~

Got my wish—six days later I wanted to kill myself again.

I remember trying to study in a group for my exam the following day . . . made progress, but I knew my depression was right there, ready to swarm.

I had dinner with my parents afterwards. I could no longer run from it. The beast throttled me, reduced me to a blob of agony. Mum and Dad spoke to me but I couldn't talk back. I just didn't have it in me. I was too drained. Too exhausted. There was nothing left but pain.

The next day

Woke up feeling ghastly. Dad drove me to uni for my exam. Silence all the way.

He dropped me off. I dragged myself to the exam room in a soulless, debilitated shuffle. When I got there I fell to the floor, sat slumped against the wall. My classmates talked to me, asked me questions, but still . . . nothing.

We got called in.

'Ten minutes reading time, starting now,' the announcer said.

I tried to read. I understood the words on their own, but put together they made no sense. I flicked through the exam. Not much of it did.

The exam itself began. I reread questions I knew I'd studied for, but in the moment the answers were a blur. I felt like I was in a trance. The world seemed a black hole. A vacuum of agony. I couldn't see any escape. The only possible salvation seemed death.

I scribbled down a few answers before the end of the exam.

'How did you go?' one of my friends asked. But I just shook my head and shuffled spiritlessly away.

I pulled myself into the streets. It was pouring down with rain. I had no idea what to do next. *Should I go home? Go back to uni and study? Go to a coffee shop? Call a friend? Get smashed at a bar?* Every possibility seemed brutally unbearable. The only one that didn't was killing myself. As you know, I'd always thought suicide was selfish, because even though it might've given me peace, I knew it would've left my family in ruins. But right then, on what was, unquestionably, the worst day of my life to date, I started to think that maybe I was wrong. I started to think that perhaps I'd been too narrow-minded.

Because I swear, I vividly remember thinking, *if my family knew how depressed I am right now . . . if they could comprehend the gut-wrenching severity of the pain I'm in . . . I swear they'd want me to put myself out of my misery. I swear they'd want me to end it all and finally be free.*

It was a dangerous revelation.

Does this mean I can die now? I thought. *Guilt-free and with my family's blessing?*

I stopped walking, let the rain pound down on top of me.

Can I do it? Can I really kill myself? Jump in front of a speeding car and join the rest of the road toll casualties?

I stood at a right angle to the road, watched the cars zooming by.

Is this really it? Can I really end it all right here?

My mind was a warzone. So much conflict. But eventually there emerged a definite answer.

No.

I can't do it.

It's the answer I'd always reached, but this time, the reason was different.

It wasn't for me.

It wasn't even for my family.

It was for those less fortunate than me.

Regardless of how depressed I feel right now, I thought, *I know that I've been tremendously blessed: with a loving, supportive family; with First World privileges; and with the opportunity and the ability to do whatever I want to in life. Regardless of how I feel right now, I have had a lot bestowed upon me, and I have to use my good fortune to help others who aren't as immensely privileged as I am. If I kill myself, Open Skies will disband. All the charity work I'd planned on doing will never get done. I'd be abandoning all the people I have the capacity to help. And no matter how much pain I'm in I just can't do that. To whom much is given, much is expected. I can't kill myself. Not now, not ever.*

I felt it so strongly, with such paramount force that it couldn't be doubted. It was as if it was a calling, a message from God in my hour of need:

I put you on this earth for a reason, Danny. You can't leave it. There's so much work that you need to do . . .

So I stepped away from the road. I called my mum.

'Hello?'

'Ma . . .' I croaked.

'Danny? Are you alright?'

I murmured something inaudible.

'Danny?' she panicked. 'Is everything OK?'

'Come and get me . . . please. Wynyard.'

I met her there, crawled into the car, muttered in broken sentences what happened.

'Danny, we would *never* want you to kill yourself!' she stressed. 'Never, ever, ever, ever! Suicide is a permanent solution to a temporary problem! You know that, don't you?'

I eventually managed to nod my head. From the corner of my barely opened eye, I saw Mum fighting back tears as she tried to drive through the rain. At some point she pulled over to call my dad. She talked to him while I sat motionless in the front seat.

After a long time, she finally hung up.

'Danny . . .' she murmured. 'Danny we think . . . we think it's time you be admitted to hospital.'

She paused solemnly.

'What do you think?'

I just wanted to get better. I was so tired of feeling sick and I just wanted to get better.

'OK,' I managed to say. 'I'll go to hospital.'

~~~

Arrangements were made and I was placed on the waiting list for a psych ward recommended by Dr Gregor, in all likelihood to be admitted in the next couple of days. Just knowing that I was about to go to a place where I could get better was enough to lift my spirits, so much so that I could crack a smile here and there and even joke around a bit with my brother. The way I saw it, going to hospital was a reason to be positive. In hospital, I'd have daily access to a psychiatrist, I'd be doing group therapy two or three times a day, and I'd have nothing to focus on except getting well again.

With all the support I'm going to get, hopefully I can get healthy again and return to life a healthy, stable human being, I thought.

~~~

Mum drove me to the hospital. I filled out some forms at reception and was then shown to my four person dorm. I sat pensively on the bed, waiting for my appointment with one of the in-house psychiatrists. It may sound a little strange, but I actually found myself hoping that she'd diagnose me with bipolar disorder. Of course it wasn't an illness that I wanted to have, but at least it would explain why the previous month had been so consummately fucked up, and hopefully with the right treatment I'd be able to get better. Being in that limbo where I didn't know what was wrong with me, where I oscillated from being horrifically depressed to being mad as a hatter . . . I couldn't take it anymore. I was desperate for answers. Sometimes anything's better than not knowing.

~~~

An hour later, I saw the psychiatrist and told her everything, and she concluded that I had "medicine-induced bipolar disorder". The bipolar part didn't come as a surprise, but the "medicine-induced" part was a hell of a shock.

'What . . . what do you mean, exactly?' I asked.

'The medication you were taking had a bad reaction with your brain, and it's caused you to develop bipolar disorder,' she said.

So it turned out that Mum was right—I should never have been taking that medication. My doctor was a quack. A bad apple. A person who I trusted who then completely fucked me over. You'd think I would've been furious at him, but anger was really the furthest emotion from my mind. Hell, I'd just been told that I had a life-threatening illness—did it really matter how I got it? I just wanted to do whatever it took to get it under control. I wasn't going to dwell on how it happened or feel pissed off or bitter or sorry for myself. I knew that wouldn't get me anywhere. Instead, I was going to focus on getting myself healthy. Anything that was taking away from that was just wasted energy.

The psychiatrist and I kept talking.

'Is bipolar disorder a permanent illness?' I asked. 'I know depression is generally more of a temporary affliction—something one often suffers from for a period of time before they at some point overcome it. But how long does bipolar disorder usually last for?'

I swallowed apprehensively.

'Is it something I'll have to battle for the rest of my life?'

'It's hard to say, Danny,' the psychiatrist said. 'Most people who have it do need treatment for the rest of their lives. But in saying that, bipolar disorder is very manageable. Through a combination of medication, therapy and maintaining an active, healthy lifestyle, many patients become stable enough that they can live a happy life that isn't impeded by their illness.'

~~~

After five days at the psych ward, I began to feel immensely better. When I switched from the antidepressant to a mood stabilising medication I stopped feeling suffocated by depression, and also ceased to experience the madness of mania. For the first time in weeks I was on a fairly even keel, and felt like I could think clearly again. Things were definitely looking up.

But in saying that, I found myself living in constant trepidation. Every day I'd go to group therapy and see 30, 40, 50, 60 and 70 year olds tell the same old stories:

'I've been depressed for the better part of my adulthood.'

'My bipolar disorder has had me in and out of hospital ever since I was 25.'

'Mental illness is just a part of who I am. I've learned to live with it, but I know I'll never beat it. It will be with me until the day I die.'

Being in the psych ward made me realise that this was my biggest fear: being forever shackled by my illness. Not being able to live a normal life. Hell, just not being happy. I would never give up on happiness—after everything I'd been through, I knew that about myself. *But what if the balance of chemicals in my brain prevents happiness from ever being possible? I thought. What if my life is genetically predetermined to be a ghastly rollercoaster where I oscillate between insufferable depression and delusional madness? What if my destiny is this: a psych ward. I feel much better now, but how long will it last? Is a relapse through hell inevitable?*

~~~

But after ten days in hospital, I had my answer.

No.

My brain chemicals do not control my destiny.

I—Danny Baker—control my destiny.

Through group therapy, I learned a lot more about the 30, 40, 50, 60 and 70 year olds who had been persecuted by their illness for decades of their life.

A lot of them drank.

Many of them were overweight, continued to eat unhealthily, and admitted to not exercising.

They had only tried a handful of medications.

They had only read one or two self-help books.

They didn't actively see a psychologist and never had for an extended period of time.

I was so surprised when I heard this. All I could think was, *how can they have such a serious illness and not do any of the right things to combat it?* At some point I delicately asked as much.

'I saw a psychologist for a couple of sessions, but I didn't like it much so I stopped going,' one said.

'Self-help books are a drag.'

'I like eating junk food.'

'Exercise is hard work!'

'I've tried a few different medications. None of them worked.'

And the most universal conclusion:

'Depression is just a part of me. I've accepted it. I know I'll probably be back in this psych ward next year sometime, but that's just who I am. Why fight it?'

I was flabbergasted. I couldn't believe it. I felt like saying:

'Mate! It doesn't have to be who you are! There are dozens of different medications on the market—how do you know that one of the ones you haven't tried won't work?

'You live in Sydney—there are hundreds of different psychologists here. You've tried a couple, but how do you know that another one won't be able to help you?

'What about all those self-help books? There are dozens of them written by some of the best psychologists in the world. Thousands of people have claimed that they've changed their life. Isn't it possible that you might get something out of them?

'And eating healthily, sleeping well, exercising frequently and not drinking are the most basic principles of managing a mental illness. Don't you think you'd feel better if you abided by them?

'How can you just surrender yourself to your illness before you've thrown everything but the kitchen sink at it? There's so much you haven't tried. You've barely scratched the surface. You can fight it! You can beat it! Depression does not have to be destiny!'

But I couldn't be so blunt. The most I could do was gently ask if one of these options may be of help to them. So I did. They shrugged. Someone changed the subject and that was the end of it.

And that's when I reached the conclusion that I controlled my own destiny. *Depression and mania and psych wards do not have to be a permanent feature of my life,* I realised, *because the means exist for me to conquer this illness.*

The means exist for me to live a happy, healthy life like any other bipolar-free person, and if I do the right things, I will. So for the rest of my life I will eat healthily, exercise frequently, and lay off the grog and other substances. I will never stop honing the techniques I've learned to prevent me from getting manic or depressed. I currently feel stable on the medication I'm on, but if at some point down the line I find myself struggling again, I will work with my psychiatrist to up the dosage or change medications.

I'm not going to let this illness beat me. I'm going to fight it and fight it and fight it until I get better. I'm going to fight it and fight it and fight it until I'm happy again.

December, 2010

After two weeks I left hospital feeling infinitely better than when I arrived, ready to return to life a healthy, re-energised man. I was looking forward to starting work on my honours thesis for 2011, and I couldn't wait to get back to submitting my novel to literary agents and working to get Open Skies' License to Fundraise as soon as possible. I felt good. Hospital was great for me—exactly what I needed. But I never wanted to go back there again. And I planned on doing everything in my power to make sure I didn't.

PART IV

OR

LEARNING HOW TO BE

HAPPY

January, 2011

At the start of the new year, everything went haywire at uni. My Economics Honours application was rejected because it turned out that I hadn't done one of the pre-requisite subjects. It was never clear that that subject was a pre-req—it was a zero credit point *law* subject—so I spent days sending emails all over the faculty trying to talk them into letting me do honours regardless, or at the very least, letting me do the pre-req concurrently with honours. But they weren't having a bar of it.

'Rules are rules,' they said. 'You'll just have to wait to do honours in 2012.'

Wait until 2012? Are you fucking kidding me? I thought. *All for a zero credit point law subject that couldn't be any less related to economics?*

It was exasperating. Uni-wise I'd had everything planned out, but this technicality had completely fucked everything up. I was so pissed off about it, but there was nothing I could do. Studying honours that year was no longer an option.

I spent the next few weeks trying to work out what to do instead, and finally decided to just complete my law degree. It definitely wasn't ideal—I'd wanted to quit law, remember? For months my plan had been to do honours and then a Masters of Applied Finance. But I knew a law degree would open the same doors for me, since many of the skills you learn studying law are also useful for management consulting. And if it meant not delaying my corporate career another year, then I preferred to just suck it up and finish it over the next two years, even though I didn't like it very much. The way I saw it, anything was better than stalling my career another year. *I've already pushed it back by writing in 2009,* I figured. *I'm behind the 8-ball enough already—all the scholarship holders I started uni with are about to finish and enter the workforce—so I can't fall behind anymore. I have to study law. I don't have a choice. I wish I didn't have to but I don't have a choice.*

February, 2011

By this point in time I'd wanted to have been signed by a literary agency, but unfortunately I was still at the start of the long, rocky, winding road that would hopefully lead to publication; the agents who I'd submitted my query letter to in September and October had rejected me, and due to having been so sick, then going to hospital, then studying for and resitting the exams I'd missed, and then having to sort out all the drama at uni, I hadn't resumed since. On the bright side, however, one agent in particular gave me some valuable feedback on the start of my manuscript—she said that she didn't like my use of a prologue to open the novel, and recommended a few other ideas. I didn't agree with her, and I knew my mentor Nick was a big fan of the prologue, but I was always open to constructive criticism, so I was experimenting with her suggestions before I got back to querying other agents. To date, the process hadn't gone as smoothly as I would've liked, but I was still optimistic. There were literally dozens and dozens of agents I hadn't queried yet, and I was praying every day that one of them would pick me up and then go on to make my dream come true.

March, 2011

I'd been working hard to get Open Skies off the ground, but we were still stuck trying to get our License to Fundraise. The relevant government department was stretched so thin that it was taking forever. They'd receive our application, take three months to review it, ask for additional information, take another three months to review that, then ask for even more information, etcetera, etcetera. It was a frustrating process, but I was hopeful we'd get our license soon so that we could get straight to work.

In the meantime, I was volunteering with a few other charities. I was doing a second stint with 180 Degrees, this time doing pro bono consulting for an organisation that was combatting sex trafficking in South East Asia. The second NGO I was working for was the Australian League of Immigration Volunteers (ALIV), who worked with refugees in community detention. In January I volunteered at a holiday camp where we spent a week taking disadvantaged children to the beach, theme parks and other fun places to brighten up their day, and since then I'd been involved in ALIV's monthly weekend program where we did the same thing. Thirdly, I'd been visiting an online mental health forum to lend an ear to sufferers who needed someone to talk to, and to try and offer them the support of a person who'd been there. It was all so eye-opening, and as charity work had always done to me in the past, it hammered home just how lucky, just how immensely and richly blessed, I really was.

How else can I feel, I remember thinking, *when I hear stories of thousands of girls as young as five or six being sold into prostitution by their very own families? How else can I feel when I hear about them being tortured, beaten unconscious or having a bucket of live snakes or maggots dumped on them as "punishment" for fighting back when a violent client tries to rape them? How else can I feel when I hear about how their vagina often rips during sex so they get infected with AIDS and die before they're 20?*

Then there were the refugees. *How can I not feel tremendously grateful for the education I've received when I do reading practice with a 15 year old from Sierra Leone who can't pronounce the word "football"? How can I not feel even more grateful for being raised in a nurturing, peaceful country like Australia when every afternoon at camp an eight year old boy from Iran begs me to sit with him by the Parramatta River and silently gaze at the soothing, tranquil water because it "relaxes" him? Or when I meet a child who's fresh off the boat from some other war-ravaged country but whose family didn't make it to the Promised Land with him?*

And then of course there was everyone I'd speak to who had a mental illness, and it was those people, more so than anyone else, who made me realise just how good I really had it. *I mean how else can I, of all people, not feel inexpressibly thankful for all the treatment I've received when I talk to teenagers who are suicidal, manic or psychotic yet whose parents "don't believe in mental illnesses" and thus refuse to get them help? I mean fuck, these kids were me last year! Particularly the ones who have bipolar disorder—they're as unstable, suicidal and deluded as I was. But my parents had been supportive. They were kind, and loving, and got me the help I so desperately needed.*

And it got me to thinking:

Where would I be right now if I hadn't had anyone to help me? If my parents were like these kids' parents and said the whole thing was a farce and that if I didn't snap out of it they'd kick me out of home?

I certainly wouldn't have recovered, so they inevitably would've thrown me out.

There's no way I could've held down a job being that sick, so where would that have left me?

Homeless?

Probably.

And what does life hold in store for a homeless man who's gone completely mad?

Nothing.

Except death.

April, 2011

You may have been wondering when I started writing *I Will Not Kill Myself, Olivia*.

The idea first came to me when I re-read my favourite novel *Candy* by Luke Davies for the fourth or fifth time:

In the same way that Candy *is a gritty story that explores the lives of two lovers who are both trapped in the throes of a heroin addiction, I could write about something similar that's centred around mental illness instead of addiction. If there's one thing I know it's depression, and I think I could draw on everything I've been through to write a really engaging fictional story.*

These same musings were also holding me back from submitting *Chrysalis* to more literary agents, because I knew *I Will Not Kill Myself, Olivia* would overlap with it to some extent. Like I've said, while I was suffering from depression I started inserting a lot of my own experiences into it, and I wasn't sure how it would work having some of the same stuff in another novel. And there was no doubt in my mind that *I Will Not Kill Myself, Olivia* had far more potential than *Chrysalis* ever did. While I thought *Chrysalis* was a good story, I could admit that there was probably nothing special about it—nothing that made it stand out from all the other books on the market. But I was confident that *I Will Not Kill Myself, Olivia* could be exceptional. *At this point in my life it's the best book I have in me, so don't I owe it to myself to write it and see what happens? But then what about* Chrysalis? *What's the best thing to do with that?*

I kept thinking.

~~~

Apart from trying to work out what to do with my novel, I was also studying law full-time—and I wasn't enjoying it at all. Every day I'd sit through hours of lectures that I couldn't care less about.

'The identification of the ground of judicial review is contingent upon which remedial model is applicable. Under the "common law remedial model", the overarching question is whether an error which gives rise to a particular ground of review can be classified as a jurisdictional error, because some remedies (specifically, prohibition and mandamus) only issue for such errors. If it cannot, the error may still attract a remedy (i.e. certiorari) if it is an "error of law apparent on the face of the record".'

Who gives a fuck? I remember thinking. *This shit is boring as hell.*

I wish I didn't have to study law. I hate it that I'm trapped in this life. But it is what it is. This degree's just something I have to suck up and finish, regardless of whether I like it or not.

May, 2011

I kept going back and forth on what to do with my writing. Sometimes I thought I should just submit *Chrysalis* because I'd spent three and a half years writing it and it would be a waste not to. But most of the time I thought I should go with *I Will Not Kill Myself, Olivia* because it was a much better concept, and if it was a choice between the two, then I owed it to myself to produce the best manuscript I could.

I met up with Nick to talk it over.

'*Chrysalis* is a good book, but it's not a great book,' he said.

'But this new idea . . . it could be.'

He was confirming what deep down I already knew. Decision made.

On the drive home, I felt exhilarated. I felt so amped up, so full of life. Just giddy for it. I was about to start writing the story of my soul, and I couldn't wait to jump right into it.

~~~

So I began writing *I Will Not Kill Myself, Olivia*, and it was going great. Whenever I'd start I'd get so absorbed in the plot, so enveloped in the characters' lives, so lost in my imaginary world that I'd never want to stop. I knew I had to be careful, though—this was the same sort of thing that had gotten me into trouble during my first degree—too much writing and not enough studying. So I made a rule: *I can only write after I've finished all my law readings for the day.* I thought that would prevent me from getting the balance out of whack.

Another thing I thought it would do was give me some extra (and much needed) motivation to get my law work done. I'd been falling behind in class, purely because I disliked it so much. Whenever I'd study I'd get so bored and frustrated and miserable that before long I'd get fed up and stop. It was awful. There wasn't a single thing in any one of my subjects that interested me in the slightest.

I wish it didn't have to be this way, I remember thinking. *I wish I wasn't forced to do something I hate. I wish I could just forget about law and write all day. What a wonderful, invigorating life that would be. What a beautiful, ethereal existence.*

What a fantasy.

June, 2011

In the past, it had taken me by surprise. It had shocked the shit out of me. It had seemingly come so out of the blue that I hadn't known what had hit me. But this time, it was almost expected.

It was back.

That harrowing despair. That anxious dread. That feeling that life is so overwhelming, so insufferable that I wished I was dead.

Depression.

This time, my relapse was the consequence of being forced to do something I hated, hour after hour after hour, day after day after day. My exams were in a week, but I couldn't study for 20 minutes before depression would paralyse my mind and coerce me to stop. I just loathed it so much that I wouldn't be able to go on. So I was up Shit Creek. I was completely fucked. And the more I fell behind, the more depression strangled me. Every day it squeezed tighter and tighter, so tight that I was gasping for air, I was spluttering like mad and I wanted to kill myself again.

'I fucking hate law,' I told Mum one night. 'It's making me so miserable . . . so suicidal. I'm a wreck again. I need to go back to the psych ward—get some help so that I can put myself back together.'

Mum nodded solemnly.

'That sounds like a good idea, Danny. If you think you need to go back to the psych ward, then you should go.'

She paused.

'I also think it would be a good idea for you to drop out of law.'

I flinched.

'W-what . . . ?' I stuttered.

'If it's making you so miserable then I think you should quit.'

I was speechless.

'I c-can't . . . I can't do that,' I finally stammered.

'Why not?'

'Because . . . because I . . . because I need a law degree to get into a good management consulting firm. A bachelor's degree isn't enough.'

'What about an honours degree?'

'What do you mean "what about an honours degree"? I couldn't do honours this year. I hadn't done the pre-req, remember?'

'But you've done it now. So why don't you just quit law and do honours next year, which is the course you wanted to do all along anyway.'

'But I can't do that. I can't delay my corporate career any longer. Don't you get it? I *have* to finish law. I don't have a choice!'

'Of course you do, Danny. You always have a choice.'

'No I don't—'

'Yes you do, Danny. You always have a choice.'

July, 2011

Over the next few weeks I spent a lot of time talking to my parents, with the aftermath being that I decided to quit law and do honours in 2012 instead. Mum and Dad helped me realise that I do in fact have choices in life, and that it's a mistake to travel a path that isn't right for me—which law sure as hell wasn't. It may've been good for my corporate career, but all it was doing was rushing me straight back to the psych ward. So I decided that that was the end of it. And when I quit, I stopped feeling depressed. I felt well again. Of course I did—I was no longer spending my days doing something I hated.

I also came to be at peace with the fact that I was delaying my career another year. Something my parents and Dr Gregor helped me understand was that I had to go through life at my own pace. I couldn't be comparing myself to others and thinking that I'd "fallen behind". There was no such thing as "falling behind". What everyone else was doing was irrelevant. I had to do what was right for me. And if that meant that I entered the workforce a little later than everybody else, then that's what it meant.

It was a period of realisations for me. As anyone who knows me will tell you, I'm a diehard NBA basketball fan, and around that time I started thinking a lot about something that Oklahoma City Thunder coach Scott Brooks had said:

'Even though we finished third last in the league in 2009, the whole year I was telling my guys, "we're not losing games . . . we're learning how to win them".'

Over the next two years, the young Thunder continued to get more experienced, and after a while began to reach their potential. In 2011, instead of finishing 28th in the league, they finished in the top four, losing to the eventual champion Dallas Mavericks in the Western Conference Finals.

'We're not losing . . . we're learning how to win.'

I loved the inherent positivity behind it, loved the implication that as long as the Thunder were learning as they lost, they would inevitably start winning. The notion struck a chord with me, and it got me thinking about my mental health.

I could say a similar thing about my illness: I could say that I'm not suffering from depression, but that instead, I'm learning how to be happy. I'm learning how to be happy because I'm learning to understand myself better. I'm learning what triggers those plummets into despair. I'm learning, through therapy, how to pick myself back up again whenever I do take a plunge. And, I'm learning valuable life lessons from my parents and my psychologist that I'll carry with me for the rest of my life. It's as if there's a fortress surrounding my brain that's there to protect me from getting depressed, and every time I learn a bit more about how to be happy, another armed guard gets posted outside it. Sure depression's army still gets through from time to time, but that just means there aren't enough guards defending it yet. But if I keep learning how to be happy like I have been over the last few weeks, then— combined with diligently taking my medication, eating well, sleeping well and exercising frequently—I'll eventually have so many guards protecting me that depression's army will be shut out for good. It'll have no way of getting through.

If they stay together, then I think it's only a matter of time until the Thunder win the championship.

Just like I believe it's inevitable that I'm going to beat my illness.

~~~

Since I'd quit law, I was back to writing full-time again. This was more like it!

It's hard to describe the pleasure writing gave me. I tried on numerous occasions to articulate it, but I was never able to come up with a perfect explanation. The best I could do was say that, when I was writing, and when I really lost myself in it, I felt as if I was transported to a different place. All my pain just melted away, and I felt at peace with the world. I felt blessed to be alive. I felt more blessed than ever to be me. I felt a pulsing rush . . . of excitement, of joy, of inspiration, all at the same time. I felt invigorated. I felt alive. I felt free. And above all else, I felt happy. Purely and utterly happy.

October, 2011

Towards the end of the year, 180 Degrees announced its first ever international consulting project, in partnership with a grassroots organisation in Cambodia that ran a range of programs supporting underprivileged children who'd been the victim of physical and/or sexual abuse, parental neglect, human trafficking, or had been orphaned. I was fortunate enough to have been selected as part of the team, and in December we were set to start looking at ways in which the organisation could achieve their long term objectives before flying to Cambodia in February for two weeks to work closer with them and help out on the ground. I was really looking forward to meeting the team and starting the project, and also to volunteering in another Third World Country. Open Skies was still in the process of getting its license, and until I could really get going with that, I relished the opportunity to support other charities.

November, 2011

At the start of the month I sent the first draft of *I Will Not Kill Myself, Olivia* to Nick, and while I was waiting for him to read it, I started doing some preparatory work for honours the following year—revising a lot of the bachelor's degree material I'd need to know and doing some early research for my thesis. I wanted to get a head start, because my goal for honours was to get the university medal.

It would do wonders for my corporate career, I thought. *If I was able to get it, I'd be almost guaranteed to be accepted into my choice of Ivy League school to study a Masters of Applied Finance, and then I'd be in a prime position to get a job at one of the top management consulting firms in the world. The upside is so big that I have to go for it. I have to do whatever it takes to try and get the medal.*

Economics was my forte—I knew I could do it. But I also knew that I'd have to be more dedicated than I'd ever been. To average 90%, I'd need to have a near-perfect mastery of the subjects, and I'd also need to write a killer thesis. It was doable, but there was no margin for error. I knew I'd need to study really, really hard. I'd have to put absolutely everything I had into it. I'd have to go for it to the exclusion of almost everything else.

But then it got me thinking, *what about my writing? When am I going to get a chance to work on my novel if I'm pulling 12 hour days busting a gut to get the medal? These last six months have been incredible, being able to dedicate myself solely to the thing I'm passionate about. I've always known it wouldn't last, that I'd have to scale it back once uni started— but the way honours is shaping up now, I don't see how I'm going to have time for it at all. And if I can't write, if I have to shun the thing I love, then how will it be possible for me to be happy?*

~~~

The tension continued to mount in my troubled mind.

I really want the medal for all the doors it will open, but how can I not write for a year? I'll be miserable if I don't write for a year, but given my corporate world goals, I won't be able to live with myself if I don't go for the medal, either. So what am I supposed to do?

Balancing life's competing priorities like work, family, friends, hobbies, exercise, relaxation, travel, volunteer work and spiritual devotion is something a lot of us struggle with, and I strongly believe that finding the right harmony is one of the biggest keys to good mental health. At its core, it requires you to have the self-awareness to be able to answer one very important question:

What makes me happy?

And at that point in my life, I still wasn't able to answer it. I wanted to do what was best for my corporate career, and I wanted to do what was best for my writing, but both options were mutually exclusive. My "balance" seemed destined to get completely out of whack the following year, and there seemed to be no way to keep it at a stable equilibrium. I felt like I was imprisoned in a Catch22, where the only possible outcome was depression. And in anticipation of being depressed all through 2012, I once again fell into a horrific depression then. All the excitement, the inspiration, the vivacity, the liberation of the past five months vanished, and I was back to feeling suicidal every day. Every day was once again choked with excruciating misery, and was once again a ghastly war I won if I didn't kill myself. And as was so often the case, my suffering triggered the urge to drink. I started having those nights again where I'd be clutching my hair on the edge of my bed, sweating through my clothes, panting through gritted teeth, desperately trying to fight off the cravings. Usually I wouldn't give in, but on one occasion the pain was so overwhelming that I thought *who gives a fuck if I have a drink,* so I went out and had 20 or 30. I stumbled home and wanted to keep drinking, so I opened the liquor cabinet and got another bottle to take to bed with me.

'Please put it back,' my mother pleaded. 'Please, please put it back.'

'I need it, I need it! Don't you get how much I need it?'

'Danny I'm begging you!' she cried. 'Please put the bottle back . . . please . . . *please* . . .'

It was such an ugly scene that I eventually did so out of guilt, but that didn't stop the cravings, it didn't stop the pain, and that's why I started experiencing the insatiable impulse to cut myself. At times I just wanted to get a steak knife from the kitchen and rip it through my flesh. I wanted to slash up my arms and watch the blood spurting out, just so I could feel something different, just so I could escape my psychological agony, just so I could release some of my built-up fucking tension and try to settle down a bit.

The urges were so strong—to drink, to cut myself, to kill myself. But I knew that drinking was a mistake, I knew that cutting myself was an even bigger mistake, and I damn well knew that killing myself was the ultimate mistake. No matter how overwhelming the desire, I knew I couldn't give in. I knew I had to keep on fighting.

Hang in there . . . don't give up . . . trust the Lord, he knows what's best, I'd tell myself. I knew I could get better, but I also knew that it would take work to do so. I knew that what I needed to do was take a time-out from everything and resolve the conflict that I needed to resolve.

So I organised to go back to the psych ward.

~~~

A few days later, I was admitted. Mum and Dad drove me there. We talked a bit on the way. Well, they talked—I mumbled what I could. Mostly there was silence. Hell, we were on the way to a psych ward. It wasn't exactly a joy ride.

After I got settled into my room I saw my psychiatrist. She decided to give me an additional medication to take on top of the sodium valproate I was already taking. It was sure to help stabilise my mood, but I knew I couldn't just rely on the drugs. I knew I needed to put in the hard yards myself and sort out my problems from within. Only then was I going to get lastingly better.

~~~

For the first few days after I started taking my new medication I was too drowsy to do much, but on my fourth day I was feeling much more with it. I took Dr Gregor's advice and started reading a self-help book by the world-renowned psychologist Dr Martin Seligman called *Authentic Happiness*.

By page 14, I'd learned the lesson that I'd needed to learn to work my way out of my despair.

~~~

On page 13 going on 14, Dr Seligman speaks of doing activities that leave us feeling invigorated, and of doing activities that leave us feeling drained. If my interpretation of the text is correct, what he's basically saying is that you will have greater happiness in your life if you do more of what leaves you feeling invigorated and less of what leaves you feeling drained.

The idea resonated very strongly with me, because the dichotomy Dr Seligman speaks of so perfectly characterised how I felt after writing and studying economics. Writing left me feeling inspired, and exhilarated, and completely alive. But studying economics—even though I found it somewhat interesting—would leave me feeling mentally exhausted. It would leave me feeling like a flogged horse. Afterwards I'd just want to watch TV, or go to the gym, or play basketball, or go out with my friends—anything to clear my head and get away from it. So what Dr Seligman said got me to thinking, *what would the rest of my life be like if it was full of pursuits that left me feeling invigorated—i.e. writing—instead of pursuits that left me feeling drained—like studying economics and presumably the corporate work that would follow?*

And that's when I had my epiphany:

I would be happier if I spent my days writing instead of studying economics or working at a management consulting firm.

It was an extraordinarily powerful realisation, because I'd never contemplated the idea of writing for a living before. I'd only ever planned to publish just the one book. What actually got me writing in the first place back in 2007 was sucking at English all through Year 12 and having it mess up my perfect UAI score—getting 99.6 instead of 100. I'd wanted to prove to myself and everybody else that I could in fact be good at the written word, so I decided to write a novel, thinking I'd be vindicated if I could get it published (I know, I know, it's perfectionism gone mad—there's a reason I was getting therapy for it). Over time however that stopped being my motivation, and I wrote purely because I loved it—but even then it was always supposed to be a one-and-done thing—achieve my dream of getting published and then dedicate myself to a lucrative career in the corporate world. The idea of being a full-time author had been the furthest thing from my mind. But this revelation had unlocked that door, and now that it was open I wanted to run right through it.

~~~

By the time dinner was served at six, my entire outlook on my future had changed. I was no longer an Economics Honours student/budding management consultant who was writing a book on the side. Instead I was an aspiring author, who studied Economics Honours so that I could become a management consultant if I couldn't make it as a writer. I still wanted to have that back-up plan in place, because I didn't want to end up a "starving artist"—I still did want to be rich. *But if I can make it as an author then I'm definitely going to hop ship*, I thought. *From now on, that's going to be my focus, which means that next year, I'm not going to put off my writing and go for the university medal—instead, I'm going to keep working on my novel, and study just enough to get the minimum marks required to get into one of the schools that I want to get in to* (75-80% instead of 90%).

With that issue resolved, the balance in my life was back, and since it was, I didn't feel depressed anymore. On the contrary, I felt excited, and inspired, and elated over my newfound epiphany, and at the prospect of trying to make it as an author. I couldn't wait to get the hell out of hospital and dive headfirst into it.

December, 2011

I stayed in hospital for another seven days, but it was really just to keep an eye on things, just to play it safe more than anything else. I stopped feeling depressed as soon as I'd had my revelation, and a week later I was discharged feeling great.

Will I ever have to come back here? I recall thinking on my way out.

I hoped not. The lesson leading to my epiphany was one more very important one that I knew I'd take with me forever, and I hoped that, combined with everything else I'd learned over the years I'd been suffering from depression and bipolar disorder, that it would be enough to prevent another relapse in the future. To use my war metaphor again, I hoped I now had enough soldiers surrounding my fortress to prevent depression's army from ever attacking my brain again. But only time would tell whether my defence was strong enough. Until then, I was focused on Nick's review of the first draft of *I Will Not Kill Myself, Olivia*. He was bound to send it to me any day then, so first order of business was to get straight back to work on the manuscript.

~~~

Dear Danny,

In summary, I think this draft is a great start—the best writing I've seen from you so far. This novel is bold, raw and confronting—nothing is left at home—and the writing style suits it well—it's fast and edgy like the protagonist. The whole notion of depression/suicide is also very topical, as it is an area of life that has not been understood. A number of prominent people have recently taken their lives and brought the issue to the forefront of public consciousness. It's also a recurring theme as we look at the psyche of the post-modern world: why are so many people unhappy when we're better off, materially, then at any time in history?

But as with all first drafts, there are things that need fixing in the second. The opening chapters of the book for one are not up to par, because you don't do a good job of setting the scene. Manly in Sydney is one of the most beautiful places in the world, but you wouldn't know it from the way it's currently portrayed in your novel. You need to paint the picture properly—make the reader feel it. See my notes on the attached manuscript for ways to do this.

Aside from the opening, I thought there was much to admire in the first half of the book. It was easy to read, had good character development, some great insights, and most importantly, it felt real and authentic. Until about halfway I was rooting for Jimmy fighting against all the odds and caught up in his story. But I found the second half of the book too dark and introspective. The personal stories, day-to-day events and the characters that have leavened the story up to this point have run out, and then it's just Jimmy's depression. I think people will be interested, then fascinated, but will then feel that it's too harrowing. You want to take them out of their comfort zone, yes—and you do a very good job of doing so—but not hold them hostage.

You have created an excellent basis for a great fictional story, but to make it really exceptional you are going to have to weigh it right. This is the tricky thing about such a dark journey—particularly one that is rooted in reality. You need to get the right balance between light and dark, between informing and entertaining. Again, see my notes on the manuscript for how to do this—particularly in the second half of the novel.

Great work, keep it up.

Nick.

~~~

After almost two years, Open Skies finally got its License to Fundraise! I was so happy, and I couldn't wait to start helping the communities we'd chosen to work in. In Peru our first project was to build the greenhouses, and at the end of the year we also set up a project in Siem Reap, Cambodia, where we planned on paying instructors to teach disadvantaged women how to weave products from natural resources, which they'd then be able to sell in hotels and other markets. Like I said, I couldn't wait to start fundraising and giving back to a world that's given so much to me.

At the end of 2011, I felt like I was in a really good place. My writing was going great and Open Skies was finally ready to go. I was doing what I loved, and not surprisingly, I felt the best I'd felt in years.

PART V

OR

EAT, PRAY, LOVE: THE

YOUNG ADULT'S

VERSION

OR

STILL LEARNING HOW

TO BE HAPPY

January, 2012

I'd delayed it as long as it was wise to, but when the new year started I began feeling the pressure to come up with a topic for my honours thesis.

'You need to make sure you pick something you're passionate about,' the course co-ordinator and all the ex-students said. 'You'll have to spend the majority of the year working on it, so you'd better make sure it's something you like.'

I had a look through all the recommended topics: twenty-first century fiscal policy. Post-GFC government regulation. Labour laws and the European Union. All the shit that was happening in Greece.

Then I started researching more obscure topics: happiness economics; the economics of time; something about speed limits and accidents and politics. Whatever. Each topic seemed as boring as the next.

I felt exhausted just thinking about it, so I pushed it to the side and returned to hustling up donations for Open Skies and moving forwards with *I Will Not Kill Myself, Olivia*. The money was coming in and the paradisiacal setting of my novel was starting to come to life as I worked at painting Manly's idyllic picture: the sun, the cool ocean breeze, the clear blue sky, the salt on your lips washed away by an ice cold beer, the serenity of the beach and the great Australian outdoors. It was all going so well, but after another week I knew I had to stop for a while and get back to my thesis.

I did some more research to try and come up with a topic, but I just couldn't find anything I was passionate about. After I'd looked into practically every branch of economics there was, my mentality turned from *I need to find a topic that I'm passionate about* to *I just need to do whatever will get me a good mark.* So I spoke to one of my friends who'd gotten the university medal the previous year.

'I did my thesis on microfinance. My supervisor was amazing—if I was you I'd just pick a topic in that area and let him guide you. You'll kill it if you do.'

So that's what I ended up doing.

'What in the area of microfinance interests you?' the supervisor asked when I met up with him.

I shrugged.

'Is there any chance you can just choose a topic for me? Maybe something that *you* find interesting?'

He considered this for a moment.

I'm currently focusing a lot of my research around competition and microfinance,' he said. 'How about something to do with that?'

I shrugged again.

'Yeah. Why not.'

'OK. Well how about I give you some journal articles to read? You could have a look at them and come up with a more specific topic yourself, and then I could guide you from there.'

So that's what I started doing, plodding through journal article after journal article: *Competition and Microfinance; Competition and the Performance of Microfinance Institutions; How Rising Competition Among Microfinance Institutions Affects Incumbent Lenders; Microfinance in Times of Crisis: The Effects of Competition, Rising Indebtedness, and Economic Crisis on Repayment Behaviour; Microfinance Trade-offs: Regulation, Competition and Financing; Competition and the Wide Outreach of Microfinance Institutions;* etcetera, etcetera, etcetera.

Within the week, depression's army had blown past my soldiers and charged straight through my fortress. Only two months after I'd left the psych ward, my brain was under siege again.

February, 2012

To my grave dismay, I realised that I was about to begin an honours year I no longer cared about. I'd started my thesis and looked over the course work, and all it did was bore me senseless.

I didn't know how this had happened. I thought I wanted to do honours. I thought I'd enjoy it. But it was all just so dry and uninspiring compared to writing my novel.

'I think you'll just have to suck it up for a year,' my parents said. 'You need to do honours if you want to be able to become a management consultant.'

So I really started thinking about what it was going to be like to be a management consultant, and that's what had ignited depression's attack. For the first time I wasn't focusing on the big fat dollar signs; on the harbour-side mansion, the sports cars and the overseas holidays; and I was actually looking at it for what it really was.

Management consultants help organisations improve their performance.

And just like honours, it didn't inspire me like writing did. If I ever needed a reminder, on my second day of being in Cambodia for the 180 Degrees project, I met a man called Tok Vanna who'd been forced to fight in the Khmer Rouge against his will. When he went to get some food during a break from training, a landmine went off in front of him. He was unconscious. When he came to, he realised his arms were gone.

He said he wanted to kill himself.

'There was no future for me. What could I do? How could I get a job, get married and support a family without any arms?'

There was a grenade in a bag attached to his waist. He arched his body around and tried to reach it. He wanted to pull out the pin and end his life, but his friend saw him just in time and took the grenade away.

Tok was then taken to hospital, where he stayed for the next nine months. When he eventually left, he was too embarrassed to go back to his family and rely on them for help, so he started begging on the streets.

Months later, Tok's mother found him and took him home, but he soon had to go back to the capital city for more treatment. Tok used up all his money on hospital bills, and ended up back on the streets again.

Luckily, an aid worker soon found him, and he was given a job selling local crafts and gifts to tourists that were visiting Angkor Watt. He then fell in love, got married, and had two children. Now Tok runs his own business, selling books at a stall in Siem Reap.

'I'm very happy now,' he told me.

I took his contact details—it was such an incredible story that I had the thought of writing his biography once I'd finished *I Will Not Kill Myself, Olivia*. It was a story that the world should hear, and I thought I could use some of the proceeds to pay for his ongoing medical bills and to put his children through school.

That was the kind of thing that excited me: meeting incredible people, writing incredible stories, and giving back to the world. That's what got my juices going. But helping billion dollar organisations improve their performance? Nothing.

'But you can do all that other stuff in your free time,' my classmates said.

That was what I used to think too, before I took off the money goggles and really thought things through. Then I was asking myself, *when will I have the time to write, to really try and make it as an author, if I'm working 60, 70 hour weeks?*

'But you only get pumped that hard in your first five or ten years,' my classmates rebutted. 'It all eases up after that.'

I wasn't convinced that was always true in practice, *but even if it is,* I thought, *how am I going to have time to write when I'm over 30 and married with kids, even if the hours have reduced to around 50 a week?*

I'd worked so hard for one of those jobs without really thinking about it, because I thought all the money would make me happy. At a top tier management consulting firm, you make close to six figures in your first year out of uni, half a million after 5-7 years, and in the vicinity of a million after 10-15. You've got it made. You're as secure as can be. But now I was finally thinking realistically, and the idea of working 60 hours a week helping organisations improve their performance made me want to shoot myself.

So I was self-destructing, I was exploding at the seams.

For fuck's sake, my back-up plan's a disaster! Another one-way ticket to the psych ward and a life of relentless, agonising despair. So where the fuck does that leave me?

I felt so insecure, so vulnerable, so terrified, and more so than anything else, so horrifically suicidal. The urge to run away, to quit, to buy that automatic and put a bullet through my head was stronger than ever before.

But I knew that I wasn't going to do that. I knew exactly what my problem was, and what's more, I knew exactly how to fix it. The only question was whether or not I had the balls to do it.

I mean fuck . . . can I really abandon my back-up plan—the guaranteed, lifelong financial security for myself and my future family; the most sure-fire way of getting rich that I'm ever going to get—and instead chase some crazy artist's dream?

~~~

The questions kept coming as I tried to fight off depression's onslaught. *Can I really ditch my back-up plan? Can I really bail on management consulting after all these years to put all my eggs in one basket and try to make it as an author? What about the financial security? What about my mental health?* I was locked in turmoil. For days I kept going back and forth and back and forth, racking my brains trying to work out what to do. It helped to have someone to talk it over with, so like I'd been doing most nights, I Skyped my mum on the other side of the world.

If I work a corporate job, I know I'm going to be depressed. I know that it's sensible to have a back-up plan, and I know that management consulting is a "great job" from the standpoint that I'll make a lot of money. But what's the point if it's just going to make me suicidal and send me straight back to the psych ward? The reason I've always fought like hell to pull myself out of the abyss in the first place has been so that I could get another crack at life. It's been so that I could get another chance to be happy. And working 60 hours a week in a job I'll hate, just to make a lot of money, just so that I have a back-up if I can't make it as an author, is hardly giving myself a chance to be happy. But going all out with my writing, throwing myself into the thing I love and doing everything in my power to make a life out of it . . . *that's* giving myself a chance. *That's* listening to my heart. *That's* living the dream.'

I'd never articulated such a sentiment before. Just hearing myself say it . . . it was so obvious what decision I needed to make.

'So that's what I'm going to do,' I said. 'I'm going to forget about management consulting and just give it my all to try and make it as an author.'

'I think that's really wise, Danny,' Mum agreed. 'You have to do whatever you think is going to make you happy. Dad thinks exactly the same thing.'

I knew my parents would be supportive. A lot of parents might object to their son throwing away a safe corporate career to chase a wildly unpredictable artistic one, but my parents have never been the kind to pressure me into living the life that they want for me instead of the life that I want for myself. While they've always given me advice, they've at the same time left those decisions up to me, and given me the freedom to follow my own path. They never had any fixed ideas about what job they wanted me to have—they just wanted me to be happy and healthy. So if that meant bailing on management consulting and pursuing creative writing, then that's what it meant.

I kept talking to Mum.

'So,' she said. 'Do you think you'll be able to make it as an author?'

I'd thought that question over a thousand times that month, and I knew exactly what my answer was.

'Yes,' I said confidently. 'I really believe I can make it, because I know I have the right attitude to make my dreams come true: I have a tireless work ethic, relentless determination, and I never, ever, ever give up. I really believe in the novel I'm writing, and even though it's not ready to be published yet, I know that in time, it will be. It's inevitable that it will be, because I'll keep at it and at it and at it until it is.'

'I believe in you, Danny, and because you have a good attitude, I have no doubt that you'll eventually have a manuscript that's worthy of being published. But you still need a bit of luck. What if the agent reading your query letter is having a bad day and they just gloss it over, assume your book won't be worth publishing like the other hundreds of books being pitched to them, and then pass on it? What if the only agents that would be interested in representing you don't have the time to take on new projects? What about that interview you told me about when an agent actually admitted to at times requesting to see manuscripts based on the author's *initials*? Like you've often said, there's just *so* much luck involved. What if it doesn't fall your way?'

I'd thought a lot about that over the last month, too.

'That part's up to God,' I said. 'I trust Him.'

~~~

So I quit honours, and as soon as I did, depression's army retreated. The war was over. It had taken a lot of hard work—a lot of self-analysis to understand myself better and work out what I really wanted out of life—but like I've said, that's all part of learning how to be happy. In that respect I'd taken a huge leap forward, and as a result, I felt so liberated. So inspired. Instead of dreading my future, I was now looking at it with unbridled excitement.

This is incredible! I mean, I actually have the freedom to chase my dream! How amazing is that?

I felt so elated. So overjoyed. I couldn't wait to fly back to Sydney and start my new life.

March, 2012

When I got back home, I started telling my friends that I'd scrapped my back up plan and was going full tilt to try and make it as an author. To be honest, I didn't expect them to understand. I thought everyone would think I was crazy, abandoning what many consider to be the Holy Grail of careers to chase one that's so risky and uncertain. I thought I'd get heaps of 'what the fuck were you thinking's and a myriad of starving artist jokes. And of course I got some. But to my surprise, a lot of people thought what I was doing was really cool. And to my even greater surprise, some people even seemed . . . envious.

'I wish I could do what I'm really interested in,' one of my mates said. 'I'd really like to be a journalist, but instead I'm working 80 hour weeks at a law firm.'

'I'd love to go to the Caribbean for a year and be a scuba diving instructor,' another friend said. 'But now I'm working six days a week as a management consultant.'

'I've always dreamed of going to a little village in Africa and doing hands-on work for an NGO. Instead I'm working as an investment banker. I don't even like it. I really wish I could just do what I enjoy.'

'But you *can* do what you enjoy,' I said. 'You guys are only 23—you're still so young! If you want to be a journalist, then be a journalist. If you want to be a scuba diving instructor, then be a scuba diving instructor. If you want to work for an NGO in Africa, then work for an NGO in Africa. Now's your chance. Go for it!'

They all just stared at me, shocked, unable to say anything.

April, 2012

For the first month after I quit honours, I'd wake up every day and just write, write, write, completely smitten with my brand new life. By then the next draft was finished so I sent it to Nick, confident that I'd successfully taken on his feedback and produced what would be close to a finished product. I knew it would take him 4-8 weeks to review it, so I then got a job at a call centre to make some quick cash in the meantime. Accordingly, I spent the first two weeks of April sitting at a desk with nothing but a phone and a thick stack of paper, dialling up strangers all over the country.

'Good afternoon, may I please speak to Steve?'

'Speaking.'

'Hi, Steve! My name's Danny, I'm calling from 2evolve on behalf of the Red Cross. How are you today?'

'Oh . . . good, I guess.'

'That's good! Look I'm just calling for a quick catch up, can you spare a couple of minutes?'

'Yeah make it quick.'

'Of course! So I'm calling for a couple of reasons—firstly, I'd just like to extend a *huge* thank-you for supporting the Red Cross in the past! It's because of people like you that we can help local and overseas communities, so thanks a lot for that!'

'OK.'

'And if I may ask, do you remember what *inspired* you to give your support in the first place?'

'No. It was a long time ago.'

'No worries! And have you had a chance to keep up to date with the work we've been doing lately?'

'No not really.'

'That's OK! So look you may be aware that the Red Cross plays a vital role in times of crisis and emergencies that affect thousands of people around Australia. I'm sure you've heard all about the Queensland and Victorian floods, for example?'

'Yeah.'

'Now the Red Cross is committed to helping communities as disaster strikes, and thereby enabling victims to rebuild their lives. For example, *over $16 million* was paid out to households damaged in the Victorian floods! But even though great work is being done, thousands of people are still in need. Your support would make a big difference Steve, so what we'd like to do today is kindly invite you to re-join us as a Regular Giver and help transform the lives of thousands of people in need. Does this sound like something you might be able to do today?'

'No not today sorry.'

'That's alright, mate. Well nonetheless thanks a lot for your support in the past, and best of luck for the future.'

'Thanks, bye.'

I'd then write down the time I called Steve on a piece of paper, circle "NEGATIVE" next to his name, put it in the ever-growing "REJECTED" pile, and then dial the number on the next piece of paper.

It was so wearisomely tedious, so mind-numbingly boring, having to repeat the same thing over and over and over again, in the same fake upbeat tone, always putting emphasis on the same old words. Then there was my supervisor always breathing down my neck, demanding that I put more pressure on the person to donate: *'you can't let them off the hook so easily'*; *'you've got to rephrase the way you ask them'*; *'you've got to sweet talk them more'*. Blah fucking blah. I hated it so much. The whole time I was on the phone I'd be watching the clock—literally—just willing the time to pass faster. And then at the end of my second week, on the long bus ride home at half-past nine at night, an anxious fear took hold of me as the cold hard reality set in:

My novel isn't published.

I'm broke as fuck.

I don't have a girlfriend.

I'm 23 years old and I live with my parents.

I spend my days working a mundane, minimum wage, dead-end job that I hate.

It had started off so romantically, writing all day and living the dream. When I was doing what I loved and when I got on a roll, it was easy to see myself succeeding; it was easy to see myself in the future as a published author with bestsellers to my name and a loving, supportive family by my side. But working at the call centre had given me a preview of my future if I never in fact made it:

> *I'm 40 years old and living in a one bedroom shithole downtown. I'm still working mundane, minimum, dead-end jobs during the day to scrape by while I bust a gut writing all night, only to see my manuscripts get rejected again and again and again. I'm still single— after all, what do I have to offer a woman?—and when anyone thinks of me, it'll be as someone for whom life held so much early promise, but who in the end amounted to nothing. They'll all say, 'Danny Baker—what a gigantic waste'. And the worst part is that I'll agree with them. I'll be plagued by that thought every day of my life.*

And on that particular day, exhausted after another horrendously monotonous eight hours at work, the only future that seemed possible was the one where I didn't make it. All I could see myself amounting to was that lonely, unfulfilled, miserable man and it scared the fucking shit out of me.

The next day

Dear Danny,

I can see that a lot of work has gone into this draft, and while the second half of the book is now less dark and you've made an obvious effort to bring the love story more to the fore, there is still another draft required.

The opening couple of chapters of the novel still aren't up to scratch. You still need to do a better job of setting the scene, and on second reading, I also think you need to develop Jimmy's character better in these chapters too. We need to know Jimmy's thoughts and feelings earlier on so that we know what's driving him—so that when he falls into depression later on we understand why. At the moment we learn it too late—by which time the reader has started questioning the character and doubting his authenticity. So you need to beef the start up a lot. Slow it down, insert key scenes here and there to allow us to understand Jimmy earlier.

Like I said in my last report the middle of the book is in good shape and has some very powerful sequences, but I still think the "love" element of the story could be structured better. Some of the interplay between Jimmy and Olivia is a bit repetitive, and a couple of the incidents were non-events that didn't change the dynamic of their relationship or push the story to a new height. You need to make these occurrences more extreme to heighten the drama—you're still writing a little conservatively. Use your imagination a bit more.

I also think the ending still needs work. At the moment, it doesn't pay off on the story you've built up. It lacks real incident or punch—when I got there I didn't feel there was a proper climax to Jimmy's illness and his relationship with Olivia. You need to finish on a bang—leave the reader wanting more.

Keep at it, Danny. You have a great product here, but it still needs more work to reach its full potential.
Good luck,
Nick.

The first thing I felt when I read Nick's review was shock. I was hoping I'd fixed most of the problems with the previous draft, but now I could see that my novel was nowhere near as developed as I'd thought. As opposed to closing in on the finish line, I was still stumbling around the middle.

Then gradually, the shock wore off, and all the anxiety, all the fear that I'd felt the previous night tightened its grip around my throat, and I was once again strangled with a flurry of doubt.

Was I an idiot for bailing on such a safe, lucrative career?

Did I really make the right decision?

Was I wrong in thinking that I'm good enough to make it as an author?

I tried to fight it but the questions kept coming as the anxiety, the fear, grew stronger and stronger. I tried to picture myself achieving my dream, tried to envision the great big smile spread across my face and the tears of joy streaming down my cheeks in the moment of being offered a contract; I tried to envision myself as the happy 40 year old— as the successful author surrounded by the loving, supportive family. But just like the previous night the picture was a blur. Every day it seemed less and less attainable, and the image of that lonely, unfulfilled, miserable man became more and more vivid in its place.

~~~

A few years beforehand, the fear that I was feeling then would've plunged me into an alcohol-fuelled tailspin. It would've plummeted me into an almost suicidal depression, one that would've almost certainly culminated in another trip to the psych ward. Then again, maybe even that's giving myself too much credit—a few years beforehand, I would've never had the courage to take the risk that I was taking then.

In my first few years of uni my self-worth was predicated on being a scholarship-holding Commerce/Law student, destined to have a house on the harbour, to drive a Porsche and to take the pretty wife and kids overseas every year. There was no way in hell I could've ever given that up.

But I'd come a long way since then. By 2012, not only could I take that fear on, but through all the therapy and self-analysis I'd done, I also had the skillset to be able to stare it down and stop it from crippling me. To once again use my war metaphor, I now had enough men guarding my fortress to prevent depression's army from re-attacking my brain.

So after breakfast the next day, I sat down comfortably on my bed and took a long, deep breath. I continued breathing, in . . . and out . . . in . . . and out, gradually calming myself down as I reminded myself of the premise upon which I based my confidence, of the reason why I believed I'd be able to make it as an author.

I have the right attitude to succeed, I said out loud. *I'm so determined, so self-motivated, so disciplined. And I'll never, ever, ever quit. And with this attitude, it's only a matter of time before I produce a novel that's ready to be published. And after that, I trust God that I'll get the break I need to achieve my dream.*

Working at the call centre and then getting a disappointing book review has made me lose sight of this lately, and that's what's allowed all the fear to shoot through. And from time to time, that's going to happen. I'm travelling a difficult road, and I'm going to have setbacks. There are going to be times when I feel scared. There are going to be times when the future I want seems far from attainable. But whenever that happens, I need to remind myself that I've got everything it takes to achieve my dream. I need to remember to have faith in myself, to have faith in God, and know that so long as I do, I can make it come true.

I spent all day on my bed, repeating the same thing over and over and over again. And gradually, the fear began to fade. My confidence started to return. And even though I was in the same position I was in 24 hours previously, by the end of the day, I felt refortified. I felt optimistic. I felt ready for the challenge.

I'm going to do this, I told myself. *I don't know when it's going to happen, but I am going to do this eventually.*

Once again, I tried to picture myself in the moment of being offered a publishing contract, with that huge smile spread across my face and tears of joy streaming down my cheeks— where I'm so suffused with happiness that I can't even talk.

For the first time since I started working at the call centre, it felt real, again.

May, 2012

In its first six months of operation, Open Skies raised over $13,500 for the greenhouses project in Peru, and started funding the women's centre project in Cambodia to teach impoverished mothers how to weave products they could sell for a profit in local markets. I was really happy with our progress, and it felt great to finally be making a difference after spending two years setting the organisation up. Raising nearly $15,000 in our first few months was a hell of an effort, and it would certainly go a long way to helping those in need.

Succeeding with Open Skies also gave me an extra shot in the arm of confidence to succeed with my writing. It reinforced the idea that if I worked hard and believed in myself, then I really could achieve what I was going for. Not a day went by where I wouldn't picture my deliriously overjoyed self in the moment of being offered a contract, and I knew that I could be that person if I just kept having faith.

And at some point in May, that was the message I got tattooed across my arm:

Faith Conquers.

~~~

I saw my psychologist for my regular monthly check-up.

'How've you been doing?' Dr Gregor asked.

'Pretty well, on the whole. I quit my job at the call centre and I'm back to writing full-time again. I'm really enjoying it, and most of the time, I'm confident I'll succeed.'

We kept on talking.

'Do you still get days when you feel scared?' he asked. 'Do you still get days when you feel terrified that you're never going to get your novel published and that you'll end up a broke, lonely, miserable 40 year old?'

I nodded solemnly.

'Yeah. Sometimes.'

We explored the issue further before Dr Gregor offered me some advice.

'I think you need to focus more on the journey you're on, and less on the end outcome,' he said. 'It's going to be a while before your novel is completely finished and ready to try and publish, so there's no need to think about what's going to happen then until the moment's upon you. Right now, just enjoy yourself. After all, you're writing full-time—right now, you're *already* living your dream! Experience it to the full. Be wholly present in the moment. Enjoy it for what it is instead of fretting about whether or not you'll get published and what may or may not happen if you don't. Whenever you do stress about all that, you're only taking away from your enjoyment of this exciting journey that you're embarking upon. Later on, if you do end up getting rejected by every agent and publisher in the business, you can worry. But right now—just forget about it.'

July, 2012

My novel still wasn't published, I was still flat broke, I still didn't have a girlfriend, I was still living with my parents, and all those scholarship holders that I used to beat my brains out competing with back in the day had expense accounts and were getting paid $100,000 salaries while I barely scraped by tutoring high school and uni students.

But ever since I started living more in the moment and enjoying my journey for what it was, I was the happiest I'd been since high school.

The Bhagavad Gita, an ancient Indian Yogic scripture, says that it is better to live your own destiny imperfectly than to live an imitation of somebody else's life with perfection. And as imperfect as it may have seemed, I could definitely say that I was living my destiny.

No wonder happiness was seeping back into my life.

October, 2012

On the first Wednesday evening of October, I was peacefully reading a novel on the couch in the kitchen when I heard my phone go off.

It was an email from Nick.

I was confident yet nervous. I really did feel like I'd gotten it right this time. But then again, it wouldn't have been the first time I'd been wrong about that.

I opened the email apprehensively, my whole body tingling with anticipation.

You're nearly there, bar a few final fix-ups.

I released a huge sigh of relief. I'd done it. I'd finally done it. It'd taken me six long, hard years, but at last I'd produced a novel that was (nearly) ready to be published. I was thrilled. Completely over the moon. My dream felt so close. So close that I could almost taste it.

November, 2012

It's time I told you how I came up with the idea for the Depression Is Not Destiny Campaign.

In August, I started watching *The X Factor*, which for those who don't know is an amateur singing competition were thousands of people across the country battle it out for a record deal. I was only peripherally interested at first, but I got really hooked when I heard the story of one of the contestants, Samantha Jade. When she was 15, she got signed by Jive Records in the States, the same label as Britney Spears, Pink and Justin Timberlake. She too seemed on her way to stardom, but unfortunately things didn't quite pan out for her and after several years of setbacks, she left the singing industry. Before she auditioned for *The X Factor* in the "Over 25s" category, Sammi was working in a factory counting stock.

'I see this as my last chance for music,' she said at her audition.

I was drawn to her right away. Although our plights had been far from similar, I felt like I could really relate to her struggle—that of having a dream you put your soul into and going through hell to try and make it come true. Knowing how it feels to want something that much, whenever I'd hear her sing, all I could think was, *she is so talented. It is a joy to watch her perform. She more than anyone deserves to have her dream come true.* I'd think the same thing when I was at work, too—coincidentally at that point in time at a factory as well: *she deserves to be on the radio I'm listening to at the moment, she deserves to be on stage at her own concert—not counting stock in a factory like this.* I just wanted the best for her. I really wanted to see her succeed.

Sammi made it through to the Top 12, from which point the artists were to sing a song each week and get eliminated one by one until only the winner was left standing. For her debut, Sammi sung *Wide Awake*, which judge Ronan Keating said she sung better than Katy Perry had sung the original. But unfortunately, the public voted her into the bottom two, and it was only by the judges' vote that she got through to the next round.

Over the next few weeks I thought Sammi was magnificent—I couldn't take my eyes off her when she was on stage, and the song she'd sing would often be stuck in my head for the rest of the night. But in the fifth and seventh rounds she found herself in the bottom two again, each time just scraping through to see another day. She admitted that coming so close to being eliminated had left her feeling "very defeated", particularly since she'd had a history of setbacks and as a result of which, was already low on confidence. Testing her resolve further still was all the unwarranted hate she was receiving over social media, saying that she couldn't sing and was only on the show because she was friends with judge Guy Sebastian; the vitriol was so intense that she was even receiving death threats. It was a time when a lot of people would've collapsed and folded, but being the fighter Sammi is she kept soldiering on, kept listening to the judges and trying to get better.

'You're a great singer, but you need to connect with the viewers more,' they said. 'You need to show your personality more. You need to be a little edgier.'

She took it all on, and as the competition progressed she went from strength to strength, and Australia got to realise how nice, how genuine, how truly loveable she really was. Her confidence seemed to gradually come back, and from the semi-finals on there was no stopping her—she was absolutely spellbinding—and in late November, Australia voted her the winner. In that moment, the emotion in her face was haunting, one of the most beautiful expressions of joy I've ever seen in my life. I literally had goose bumps just looking at her. As an artist I was deeply inspired by her triumph after everything she'd been through, and as a person I was flushed with pure and utter happiness for her. It couldn't have happened to a more deserving girl, and I'm really glad I was there to witness it.

After the finale, I found myself musing about *The X Factor* in general:

It's obviously great for Sammi and the other top contestants who'll surely go on to get record deals, but to say that it only benefits the singers isn't doing it justice. On top of being a talent show, The X Factor *is a treasure trove of uplifting individual tales that transcend all realms of life, and by providing a forum for the contestants to tell their story, and for the country to then be able to follow their journey and watch them beat their demons and succeed,* The X Factor *gives hope and inspiration to viewers who need it.*

Thinking about *The X Factor* in that way then got me thinking about my own story:

If people currently suffering from depression knew what I went through and then saw me in my ardently happy moment when I've achieved my dream, then wouldn't they be inspired too? Wouldn't it give them hope that they could also recover and go on to live a happy, healthy life?

And so, the Depression Is Not Destiny Campaign was born.

EPILOGUE

October, 2013

I never thought the first few years of my adulthood would turn out the way they have. When I was 18 at the scholarship dinner, I was sure that I'd finish my Commerce/Law degree and by now be making six figures at a management consulting firm or an investment bank. Never did I think I'd fall victim to depression, become an alcoholic, found a charity, develop bipolar disorder from a doctor's negligence, go to a psych ward, write a second book, quit law, return to the psych ward, un-enrol from honours and at 24 end up a philanthropist, a mental health advocate and an aspiring author who's still broke and living with his parents. It's been a strange ride, and at times an extremely painful one, but the truth is that I wouldn't change any of it, because it's brought me to the wonderful place that I'm in right now: I'm helping impoverished communities through my foundation; I'm about to launch a mental health campaign that I hope will inspire thousands of people; and with a bit of luck, I'll soon achieve my dream of becoming a published author. Above all else, however, I am finally happy, and I can't ask for anything more than that. At last, I have enough armed men stationed outside my fortress to prevent depression's army from being able to get through again. It still tries to—I'm often getting tested by the inevitable frustrations and disappointments of life—but I now understand myself so well and my coping mechanisms are so refined that these days, I can handle all the tribulations that used to rip me to shreds.

'How did you recover?' is the most common question I'm asked.

I get the feeling that half the time the person's expecting me to have some wild, crazy explanation they've never heard of before, as if how to beat depression is one of the eternal mysteries of life. But at the end of the day, how I recovered was very simple: I never gave up on happiness, I never stopped fighting my illness, and most importantly, I got the help I so desperately needed. And if I had to identify the biggest problem surrounding the mental health industry right now, I'd probably say that it's the fact that so many sufferers fail to seek help. In all my interaction with victims in group therapy sessions, psych wards, mental health forums, charity functions and even in day to day life, I've heard a million and one reasons for why people don't get help. Sometimes it's financial, which is tragic (and even then there are alternatives), but often money's got nothing to do with it.

A lot of the time it's stigma:

'If I see a psychologist, take medication or read self-help books, then people might judge me—so no way!'

Nearly as often it's pride:

'I refuse to "get help" because I want to sort my problems out for myself. "Getting help" is weak, and if I "got help", then I'd feel like a failure.'

And of course there's also fear—of facing your demons, of going down a path unknown.

It's hard for me to relate to such lines of thinking, because I never had any of these hang-ups. I just wanted to get well again—plain and simple. If that meant seeing a psychologist, then I saw a psychologist. If that meant taking medication, then I took medication. If that meant checking into a psych ward, then I checked into a psych ward. Stigma, pride and fear never came into it—and logically speaking, it shouldn't for anyone else either. As many professionals in the field say:

'If you had a broken leg, would you get help?

If you had diabetes, would you get help?

If you had cancer, would you get help?

Of course you would.

So you need to get help if you have a mental illness, too.'

So if there's one thing I can say to the 350 million people on this planet that are estimated to have depression—and to everyone else who suffers from another form of mental illness—it is that: abandon all your hang-ups and get the help you need. I did, and it saved my life. And it can save yours, too.

Yet in saying that, I also understand that I was extremely fortunate to receive the treatment I did. My parents were very supportive from day one, and could afford to pay for my medical and psychological bills. And when I think of my experience with mental illness as a whole, it's this good fortune that really comes to mind. To the best of my recollection, at no point did I ever think of myself as unlucky for having suffered so severely. Quite the opposite—I've always thought of myself as extremely blessed to have received the help I did to beat my illness. And it's this good fortune that's motivated me to start the Depression Is Not Destiny Campaign.

'Aren't you going to find it hard?' my mum often asks. 'You'll be spilling your soul to the entire world. You'll be opening yourself up for everyone to see some of the most private, intimate moments of your life. Not to mention that mental illness still carries such a stigma—by being so open about your experiences with it, you're going to cop all sorts of criticism from all the ignorant Tom, Dick and Harrys out there. Hell, Samantha Jade was receiving death threats, and what you're doing is more controversial than singing! I do think you have the chance to help a lot of people, but you're also exposing yourself to a hell of a lot of abuse from any person with internet access.'

She's right—I'm sure I will find it hard at times. Contrary to how it may appear, I'm actually a very private person. Aside from Sylvia back in 2008 and 2009, I've hardly discussed my struggles with anyone except for my family and my medical team. Even my closest friends have no idea what I've been through—they'll read this book and be shocked as hell. So I'm sure I will find being so open quite challenging. But that doesn't mean that I'm going to let it stop me.

'You're right, Mum,' I always reply. 'But I'll take that on. The way I see it, if it wasn't for the support you and Dad have given me and for all the treatment I've received, I have no idea where I'd be right now. Maybe I'd be in a psych ward. Maybe I'd be homeless. Maybe I'd be dead. So the way I see it, I'm lucky just to be here. I'm really, really lucky just to be here. So if there's anything I can do to help someone who's in the same position I was in—particularly someone who isn't as fortunate to receive the help that I got—then I'm sure as hell going to do it.'

As Mr Williams once said to me:

'To whom much is given, much is expected.'

A (VERY) BRIEF UPDATE FROM 2016

After all I've been through, it gives me immense, immense pleasure to say that after a lot of blood, sweat and tears, *I Will Not Kill Myself, Olivia* is now on the market, has already hit bestseller status in the United Kingdom, and sells enough copies to allow me to travel around the world full-time while I write the sequel *I Just Want To Be Happy, Olivia*. And, if you liked my memoir, then I'm really, really confident you're going to like *I Will Not Kill Myself, Olivia* too, which has been described by critics as "explicitly realistic", "absolutely intriguing", "stunningly gritty", "mesmerising", "a modern day Romeo and Juliet", and "one of the most singularly powerful books about depression on the market".

To grab your copy, please visit Amazon.

After all I've been through, I can't wait to share my debut novel with you!

All my love,

Danny.

P.S. After reading my memoir, a lot of people email me asking if since its release, I've managed to keep my depression at bay – and my answer is a resounding yes! It's been almost three years since it came out, and I'm blessed to be able to say that I'm still happy and healthy and absolutely loving my life. As I like to say, depression is a liar – recovery *is* possible, even if during the thick of our depression, we don't always believe it.

BONUS CONTENT

If you'd like me to email you an inspiring, uplifting quote each morning to give you some additional support and encouragement to help you through your day, then please visit **www.dannybakerwrites.com/quotes**.

CONTACT

If you'd like to get in touch, then please do so via my website at **www.dannybakerwrites.com**.